INTERMEDIATE ALGEBRA 2ND EDITION
STUDENT RESOURCE

PRACTICE PROBLEM WORKSHEETS

Rafael Espericueta,
Bakersfield College

First published in the United States of America in 2010 by Cognella, a division of University Readers, Inc.

Printed in the United States of America

ISBN: 978-1-62131-190-4

www.cognella.com   800.200.3908

education
be smarter.

888.517.0188   www.CoDcourses.com

Dear Student,

Congratulations! By purchasing this C2 Algebra II Workbook and working with your C2 tutor, you have taken a wonderful first step towards increasing your math knowledge and getting better grades in school!

This workbook covers all of the important material you would learn in a typical Algebra II course at school.

- Linear Equations and Inequalities
- Functions and Graphs
- .Systems of Linear Equations and Matrices
- Polynomials
- Rational Expressions
- Radical Expressions
- Quadratic Equations and Inequalities
- Exponentials and Logarithms
- Conic Sections…

Please remember to bring this workbook with you to every Algebra II class at C2. You will begin each class by reviewing the previous night's homework with your teacher, and then your C2 teacher will provide instruction in the next lesson. You will show your understanding of the day's material through a series of in-class exercises and discussions.

You are REQUIRED to complete every assigned homework assignment. In addition to completing the lessons in this book, you should review what you have learned from earlier lessons every day.

Thank you for participating in this program; we hope that you enjoy your time learning with us!

—The C2 Education Curriculum Team

Also available from C2 Education:

C2 Math Series

Pre-Algebra

Algebra I

Geometry

Precalculus

C2 College Prep Series

Advanced Vocabulary

SAT Math

SAT Reading

SAT Essay

SAT Grammar

ACT English

ACT Math

ACT Reading

ACT Science

C2 Enrichment Series

Book Club

Writing Club

And many more!

Intermediate Algebra 2ND Edition
Practice Problem Worksheets

Table of Contents

INTERMEDIATE ALGEBRA 2ND EDITION
Practice Problem Worksheets

CHAPTER 1: LINEAR EQUATIONS AND INEQUALITIES

Chapter 1 Section 1: Solving Linear Equations

Problems

Solve the following equations.

1. $7x = 63$

2. $3x = 66$

3. $5x = 23$

4. $-9x = 55$

5. $-49y = 105$

6. $115y = 92$

7. $x + 10 = 0$

8. $x - 13 = 0$

9. $6y + 9 = 0$

10. $5y + 3 = 0$

11. $2x - 7 = 0$

12. $7x - 13 = 0$

13. $8p + 3 = 11$

14. $12p + 10 = 34$

15. $4x - 5 = 33$

16. $15x - 12 = 10$

17. $3y + 2 = 6y - 7$

18. $6 - 3v = 3v - 6$

19. $7z + 2 = 4z - 3$

20. $13 - 2v = 11v - 4$

21. $3Q + 7 = 6Q - 7(2 - 6Q)$

22. $8x - 3 - 9x + 1 = 4x - 3 + 2x - 6$

23. $2u + 7 - 5u = 2u - 6u + 9$

24. $A(5 - 3A) = 8 - 3A(A - 4)$

25. $4x(x - 5) + 2x(7 - 2x) = 3$

26. $5a - 2(a - 2) = 3a + 4(2a - 5)$

27. $2z[2 - (5 - 3z)] = -3[8 - 2z(z - 2)]$

28. $-4[9z - 3(3 - 2z)] = 5[2 - 5(2z - 5)]$

29. $\dfrac{7x}{4} - \dfrac{3}{20} = \dfrac{2x}{5}$

30. $\dfrac{3x}{28} - \dfrac{6}{7} = \dfrac{5}{4} - \dfrac{11x}{28}$

31. $\dfrac{2x}{9} - \dfrac{5}{72} - \dfrac{1}{24} = \dfrac{x}{18} + \dfrac{1}{36}$

32. $5 - \dfrac{4}{x} = \dfrac{5}{x} - 4$

33. $\dfrac{5}{2z} = 2 - \dfrac{4}{3z}$

34. $\dfrac{7}{3z} + 3 = \dfrac{5}{6z} - \dfrac{1}{2z}$

_____

_____

35. $\dfrac{4}{y} - \dfrac{5}{2y} = \dfrac{2}{3}$

36. $1 - \dfrac{2}{x} - \dfrac{3}{x} = 0$

_____

_____

37. $\dfrac{5}{3x} = \dfrac{7}{2x} - 2$

38. $\dfrac{7}{W} + \dfrac{2}{5W} = \dfrac{2}{3} - \dfrac{7}{15W}$

_____

_____

39. $2.3x - 1.6 = 5.3x + 2.6$

40. $0.1D - 0.2 = 0.3D + 0.4$

_____

_____

41. $0.21x - 0.45 = 0.17x + 0.22$

_____

Chapter 1 Section 2: Formulas

Problems

Solve the following equations for the variable indicated.

1. Solve for x: $5xy = 10$

2. Solve for e: $7ae = 3u$

_____

3. Solve for a: $is = at$

4. Solve for v: $4v = 2r$

_____

5. Solve for n: $2w = 3nu$

6. Solve for B: $2B = 3A$

_____

7. Solve for T: $2T = 5T - 3S$

8. Solve for D: $8D - 5E = 5D$

_____

9. Solve for E: $3 = EZ - EM$

10. Solve for L: $aL + hL = 9$

_____

11. Solve for A: $V = 4B^2 A$

12. Solve for r: $A = 2\pi rh$

_____

13. Solve for Q: $Qx = 3Wi - 4Q$

14. Solve for t: $mg = Wt + Mt$

_____

15. Solve for m: $E = mc^2$

16. Solve for m: $E = \dfrac{mv^2}{2}$

_____

17. Solve for E: $ABC = DEF$

18. Solve for A: $\dfrac{D}{BC} = \dfrac{EF}{A}$

19. Solve for Z: $\dfrac{CE}{BD} = \dfrac{ZF}{CA}$

20. Solve for h: $\dfrac{2g}{3hQ} = 3aQ$

21. Solve for A: $4A + 3B = 2AB - 7B$

22. Solve for C: $2AC - 5B = 2AB - 4C - B$

23. Solve for y: $3xy - 5Bx = 2y - 7Ax$

24. Solve for x: $3xy - 5Bx = 2y - 7Ax$

25. Solve for B: $3xy - 5Bx = 2y - 7Ax$

26. Solve for S: $\dfrac{2}{R} - \dfrac{5}{S} = \dfrac{3}{T}$

27. Solve for T: $\dfrac{2}{R} - \dfrac{5}{S} = \dfrac{3}{T}$

28. Solve for y: $\dfrac{1}{7y} - \dfrac{1}{x} = \dfrac{1}{7xy}$

29. Solve for x: $\dfrac{1}{2y} - \dfrac{1}{x} = \dfrac{1}{2xy}$

30. Solve for W: $\dfrac{A}{W} + \dfrac{2}{A} = \dfrac{3}{AW}$

31. Solve for h: $A = 3\pi r(2h + r)$

32. Solve for A: $2AB = 3B(2B - 3A)$

33. Solve for A: $AB(x-2) = C(2x-B)$

34. Solve for x: $AB(x-2) = C(2x-B)$

_____

_____

35. Solve for B: $AB(x-2) = C(2x-B)$

36. Solve for x: $\dfrac{1}{xy} = \dfrac{2}{x} + \dfrac{3}{y} - 1$

_____

_____

37. Solve for y: $\dfrac{5x+1}{xy} = \dfrac{1}{x} - \dfrac{x}{y}$

38. Solve for A: $\dfrac{A}{6} = \dfrac{2A-1}{3B} + \dfrac{A}{6B}$

_____

_____

39. Solve for B: $\dfrac{A}{6} = \dfrac{2A-1}{3B} + \dfrac{A}{6B}$

40. Solve for z: $\dfrac{xy}{z} = \dfrac{y}{x} + \dfrac{x}{y}$

_____

_____

Chapter 1 Section 3: Sets, Interval Notation, and Linear Inequalities

Problems

1. Express the graphed interval in set-builder notation:

    $$-2 \qquad 5$$

    _____

2. Express the graphed interval in interval notation:

    $$-2 \qquad 5$$

    _____

3. Graph the interval $[-1, 7]$.   4.   Graph the interval $(-1, 7)$.

    _____   _____

5. Express the set of real numbers greater than or equal to 4 in both set-builder and interval notation.

    _____

6. Express the set of real numbers less than –2 in both set-builder and interval notation.

    _____

7. Use set-builder notation to specify the set of natural numbers between 100 and 1000.

    _____

8. Use set-builder notation to specify the set of even natural numbers between 100 and 1000.

    _____

9. $\{2, 4, 6\} \cup \{1, 3\} = ?$ 10. $\{0, 5, 10, 15, 20\} \cap \{0, 4, 8, 12, 16, 20, 24\} = ?$

    _____   _____

11. Solve, graph, and express the solution in both set-builder and interval notation:
    $$3x + 2 \leq -4.$$

    _____

12. Solve, and express the solution in both set-builder and interval notation: $7 - 2x \geq 1$.

_____

13. Solve, and graph the solution. Express your solution in interval notation: $6x + 3 > 4x - 1$.

_____

14. Solve, and graph the solution. Express your solution in interval notation: $5x - 4 < 2x + 5$.

_____

15. Solve, and express the solution in both set-builder and interval notation: $8x + 1 \geq 2x + 17$.

_____

16. Solve, graph, and express your solution in set-builder and interval notation: $-2 - x < 7$.

_____

17. Solve, and express the solution in both set-builder and interval notation: $4 - 3x \leq 10$.

_____

18. Solve, graph, and express your solution in set-builder and interval notation:
$$5(1 - 2x) - 4(x - 3) \leq 19 - 10x.$$

_____

19. Solve, graph, and express your solution in set-builder and in interval notation:
$$3(4x + 3) \leq 7 - 4(x - 2).$$

_____

For problems 20-22, solve, and express your solution in both set-builder and interval notation.

20. $12 - 2(3x - 2) \geq 5x - 2(5 - x)$

_____

21. $\dfrac{2}{3}x - \dfrac{3}{2} \leq \dfrac{7}{6} - \dfrac{1}{3}x$.

_____

22. $\dfrac{3}{5}x - 2 < \dfrac{3}{10} - x$

_____

For problems 23-31, solve, graph, and express your solution in both set-builder and interval notation.

23.

$\dfrac{x+1}{4} + \dfrac{1}{6} \geq \dfrac{x-2}{3}$

_____

24. $\dfrac{x+8}{8} - \dfrac{x-2}{12} \leq \dfrac{5}{6}$

_____

25. $\dfrac{x-1}{12} - \dfrac{x}{9} \geq \dfrac{1}{18}$

_____

26. $-5 < 3x + 4 < 16$

_____

27. $-6 \le 5x + 14 \le 24$

_____

28. $0 < 2x - 6 \le 4$

_____

29. $-16 < 1 - 3x < 16$

_____

30. $3 \le 7x - 14 < 31$

_____

31. $-1 < 1 - x < 1$

_____

32. Solve, expressing your solution in interval notation: $7 \ge 2 - 3x \ge -5$.

_____

33. Solve, expressing your solution in set-builder notation: $-4 < 3 - 2x \le 1$.

_____

34. Solve, expressing your solution in interval notation: $2 < 6 - x < 4$.

_____

35. Solve, expressing your solution in set-builder notation: $\dfrac{2}{5} \geq \dfrac{3x-7}{2} > -\dfrac{3}{10}$.

_____

36. Solve, expressing your solution in interval notation: $-2 < \dfrac{1-x}{2} \leq -1$.

_____

37. Solve, expressing your solution in set-builder notation: $\dfrac{2}{3} < \dfrac{2x-1}{6} < \dfrac{5}{2}$.

_____

38. Solve, expressing your solution in interval notation: $-3 \geq \dfrac{3-2x}{5} \geq -9$.

_____

39. Solve, expressing your solution in set-builder notation: $-x \leq 5 < 2 - x$.

_____

40. Solve, expressing your solution in interval notation: $3 + x \geq 3x > x - 3$.

_____

Problems

Solve and graph the following. Express the solution in set-builder notation.

1. $4x + 1 < 5$ and $4x + 7 > -1$

2. $6x - 4 \geq 2$ and $3x - 8 < -2$

_____

_____

3. $11x - 1 \geq 9$ or $4 - 3x > 7$

4. $15x + 3 \geq 8$ and $7x - 1 \geq 13$

_____

_____

5. $3 - 4x < 12$ and $11 + 4x > 6$

6. $3x + 7 > 10$ or $15x - 12 \leq 18$

_____

_____

7. $6x - 2 < -14$ or $5x + 1 > 11$

8. $2x - 3 > 1$ and $3x - 1 < 2$

_____

_____

Solve and graph the following. Express the solution in interval notation.

9. $3x + 7 < 10$ or $2x - 1 > 5$

10. $17x - 3 \geq 21$ and $4x + 6 < 22$

_____

_____

11. $3x - 6 \geq 9$ or $2(10 - x) > 6$

12. $7(x - 2) \geq 14$ or $5x - 3 > 22$

_____

_____

13. $8 - 8x > 24$ and $5 - 3x < 17$

14. $9x - 1 > 17$ or $2x + 7 \leq -21$

_____

_____

15. $54 - 10x \leq 24$ or $11 - 5x \geq 6$

_____

Chapter 1 Section 4: Compound Linear Inequalities

Solve the following. Express the solution in set-builder notation and in interval notation.

16. $2x + 3 \leq x - 6$ or $3x - 2 \leq 4x + 5$

17. $5x + 1 \leq 3x - 2$ and $6x + 4 < 4x - 5$

18. $7 - 3x < 6x - 2$ and $7x + 5 < 2x + 7$

19. $8x - 2 > x - 3$ or $8 + 5x < 2x - 1$

20. $8 - 3x < 6 + 7x$ or $2x + 5 \geq 6x - 3$

21. $-11 - 2x \leq -8 + 4x$ and $5x - 1 \leq 4 + 3x$

22. $-x - 5 \geq 7x - 17$ and $3x + 5 < 2x + 9$

23. $-9x + 3 < -5x - 1$ or $3x - 4 < 9x - 2$

24. $-5x - 2 < 3x - 2$ or $4x - 10 < -3x + 12$

25. $7 - 3x < x + 6$ and $2x - 1 \geq 4x - 7$

Solve and graph the following. Express the solution in set-builder notation and in interval notation.

26. $4x - 8 > 6x + 5$ or $5x - 8 < x - 2$

27. $-3x - 5 \geq -5x - 1$ and $8 - 3x < 6 + 7x$

28. $2x + 5 < 3x - 1$ or $x - 4 > 2x + 6$

29. $6x + 5 < -1$ or $1 - 2x < 7$

30. $6 - 7x < 3 - 9x$ and $1 + 6x < 7x - 3$

31. $3x - 4 < -4x + 5$ and $11x - 2 > -3x + 4$

32. $3x - 1 > 2x + 4$ or $5x - 2 \leq 3x + 4$

33. $5x + 12 \geq 2$ or $7x - 1 \leq 13$

_____

_____

34. $6x - 4 \leq 1 - 4x$ and $x - 8 < 5x - 2$

35. $14 + 3x \geq 7 - 11x$ or $7x - 1 \geq 2x - 6$

_____

_____

36. $4x + 8 < 7x - 16$ and $4x - 2 < x - 1$

37. $9 - 3x < 3x + 1$ or $6x + 1 > 7x + 1$

_____

_____

38. $2x + 5 > 4x - 1$ or $3x + 19 > x + 1$

39. $x + 7 \geq 7 - 3x$ and $-3x - 11 > 2x - 7$

_____

_____

40. $3x - 19 \leq 9x + 11$ or $5x + 7 > 4x - 2$

_____

Problems

Solve the following equations and write your solutions as solution sets.

1. $|x| = 19$ 2. $|y| = 77$

    _____   _____

3. $|x| + 8 = 17$ 4. $|x| - 80 = 20$

    _____   _____

5. $|x| - 20 = -23$ 6. $|z| + 17 = 16$

    _____   _____

7. $5|x| + 1 = 16$ 8. $4|x| - 3 = 17$

    _____   _____

9. $11|2x| - 13 = 31$ 10. $7|2x| + 3 = 45$

    _____   _____

11. $|5x - 33| = -2$ 12. $|2x + 21| = -3$

    _____   _____

13. $|27x - 15| = 22$ 14. $|22x - 13| = 9$

    _____   _____

15. $25 - |7x + 26| = 13$ 16. $|18 - 4x| - 100 = -64$

    _____   _____

17. $19 - |2x + 23| = 39$ 18. $|23x - 19| + 100 = 0$

    _____   _____

19. $\left|10y - 7\right| = \left|2y\right|$

20. $\left|41w - 1\right| = \left|-12w\right|$

---

21. $\left|8x - 19\right| = \left|9 - 18x\right|$

22. $\left|12x - 31\right| = \left|6 - 17x\right|$

---

23. $\left|a - 23\right| = \left|13 - 2a\right|$

24. $\left|T + 4\right| = \left|2 - 3T\right|$

Solve the following inequalities. Graph your solutions, and express them using both interval notation and set-builder notation.

25. $\left|x\right| \leq 27$

26. $\left|x\right| < 16$

---

27. $\left|34 - 14x\right| < -37$

28. $\left|4 - 27x\right| \leq -16$

---

29. $\left|31 - 13x\right| < 33$

30. $\left|4x - 21\right| \leq 18$

---

31. $\left|4x + 31\right| \leq 23$

32. $\left|8x + 1\right| < 3$

---

33. $|8 - 7x| > -1$

34. $|28 - 19x| \geq -4$

_____

_____

35. $|12 - 21x| \geq 22$

_____

36. $|7 - 9x| > 14$

_____

37. $8 - |9x - 17| \leq 24$

38. $11 - |2x + 23| < 101$

_____

_____

39. $7 < |10x - 35| + 1$

_____

40. $23 - |4x - 9| \leq 15$

_____

Intermediate Algebra 2ⁿᵈ Edition
Practice Problem Worksheets

Chapter 2: Functions and Graphs

Chapter 2 Section 1: Relations and Graphs

Problems

Find the domain and range of the relations in problems 1-3.

1. $\{(1,1),(4,2),(9,3),(1,-1)(4,-2)\}$

2. $\{(-3,-1),(0,1),(2,6),(-1,-1)\}$

_____ _____

3. $\{(4,0),(1,0),(0,0),(2,0),(3,0)\}$

_____

For problems 4-7, determine whether the ordered pair satisfies the given equation.

4. $(-5,1);\ 2x-3y=-13$

5. $(1,-3);\ y=4-x$

_____ _____

6. $(1,8);\ y=-\dfrac{8}{x}$

7. $(3,-5);\ y=4-x^2$

_____ _____

8. Which point satisfies the equation $y=\dfrac{2}{3}x$?

   $A=\left(\dfrac{1}{3},2\right)\quad B=(3,2)\quad C=(6,2)\quad D=(6,4)\quad E=\left(0,\dfrac{2}{3}\right)$

_____

9. Which point satisfies the equation $y=x^2$?

   $A=(0,0)\quad B=(3,6)\quad C=(2,4)\quad D=(1,2)\quad E=(1,1)$

_____

For problems 10-14, complete the ordered pairs to satisfy the given equations.

10. $y=\dfrac{3}{4}x;\quad (0,\_)\ \ (4,\_)\ \ (-4,\_)$

11. $2x-3y=12;\quad (\_,-4)\ \ (9,\_)\ \ (\_,0)$

_____ _____

12. $y=2x^2-3x;\quad (0,\_)\ \ (2,\_)\ \ (-2,\_)$

13. $y=|x|+1;\quad (3,\_)\ \ (-1,\_)\ \ (-2,\_)$

_____ _____

14. $y = -\dfrac{4}{x}$ $(-4, \_)$ $(\_, -4)$ $(2, \_)$

_____

Graph each equation over the specified interval. (Hint: make a table of xy-values.)

15.   Graph $y = 2x + 4$ over the interval $[-3, 2]$.

16.   Graph $y = -\dfrac{2}{x}$ over the interval $[-2, 2]$.

17.   Graph $y = 3x - x^2$ over the interval $[-2, 4]$.

18.   Graph $y = -3x + 5$ over the interval $[0, 3]$.

19.   Graph $y = 3 - |x|$ over the interval $[-5, 5]$.

20.   Graph $y = 5 - x^2$ over the interval $[-3, 3]$.

21.   Graph $y = \dfrac{4}{x}$ over the interval $[-2, 2]$.

22.   Graph $y = x - 3$ over the interval $[-2, 4]$.

23. Graph $y = |x + 2| - 1$ over the interval $[-6,2]$. **24.** Graph $y = x^2 + 5x$ over the interval $[-6,1]$.

_____   _____

25. Graph $y = |2x + 2|$ over the interval $[-3,1]$. **26.** Graph $y = \dfrac{1}{2x}$ over the interval $[0,3]$.

_____   _____

27. Graph $y = -x + 6$ over the interval $[-2,4]$. **28.** Graph $y = -2x^2 + x - 2$ over the interval $[-2,2]$.

_____   _____

29. Graph $y = x^2 + 2x + 1$ over the interval $[-3,1]$. **30.** Graph $y = \dfrac{3}{4x}$ over the interval $[0,5]$.

_____   _____

31. Graph $y = \dfrac{1}{2}x + 3$ over the interval $[-6,1]$.

32. Graph $y = \left|\dfrac{5x}{2}\right|$ over the interval $[-2,2]$.

_____   _____

33. Graph $y = x^2 - |x - 2|$ over the interval $[-2,2]$.

34. Graph $y = \dfrac{2}{3}x - 2$ over the interval $[-2,2]$.

_____   _____

35. Graph $y = 2|x| - 1$ over the interval $[-3,3]$.

36. Graph $y = 4 - x$ over the interval $[-1,4]$.

_____   _____

37. Graph $y = -2x^2 + 6x$ over the interval $[0,3]$.

38. Graph $y = x^2 + 5x + 6$ over the interval $[-4,0]$.

_____   _____

39. Graph $y = x^2 + x$ over the interval $[-3, 2]$. **40.** Graph $4x + 5y = 20$ over the interval $[-1, 6]$.

_____   _____

Chapter 2 Section 2: Functions and Graphs

Problems

For problems 1-3, note whether or not each relation given is a function.

1. {(–2,–1), (–4,–5), (0,–1), (3,5)}

2. {(0,0), (1,1), (–1,1), (2,4),(–2,4}

_____

3. {(1,1), (4,2), (9,3), (1,–1), (4,–2)}

_____

4. What set of ordered pairs are depicted? Is it a function?

5. What collection of ordered pairs are depicted? Is it a function?

_____

6. Evaluate the function $f(x) = \dfrac{x-1}{x+6}$ at the values $x = -1, 0, 1, 2$

7. Evaluate the function $h(x) = \dfrac{2x+4}{3x-5}$ at the values $x = -3, -2, 0, 2$

_____

8. Evaluate the function $g(x) = |x-1|$ at the values $x = -1, 0, 1, 2$

9. Evaluate the function $f(x) = \dfrac{3x}{x+1}$ at the values $x = -2, -1, 1, 2$

_____

10. Evaluate the function $g(x) = \dfrac{5-x^2}{5-x}$ at the values $x = -5, -2, 0, 2, 5$

11. Evaluate the function $f(x) = \dfrac{3x^2+1}{x-3}$ at the values $x = -1, 0, 2$

_____

12. Evaluate the function $f(x) = \dfrac{4x^2 - 7}{2x - 3}$ at
the values $x = -1, 0, 3$

_____

For problems 13-19, graph the function given and specify the domain and range.

13. $f(x) = 1 - x^2$

14. $g(x) = |x| - 4$

15. $f(x) = x^2 + 6x + 5$

16. $g(x) = -\dfrac{1}{3}x + 6$

17. $f(x) = x^2 - 9$

18. $f(x) = 2 - |x|$

19. $f(x) = x^3 - 1$

For problems 20-23, state whether or not the graph represents a function, and specify the domain and range.

20.

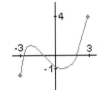

21.

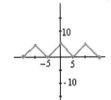

---

22. $sqrt(x) = \sqrt{x}$

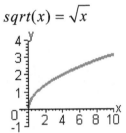

23. $x = \dfrac{10}{9} y(y+3)$

Find the domain of the functions in problems 24-30; express each in set-builder notation.

24. $f(x) = \dfrac{4}{x-3}$

25. $f(x) = \dfrac{5x}{3x+9}$

---

26. $f(x) = \dfrac{x+1}{x^2+1}$

27. $f(x) = \dfrac{2x+1}{(2x+5)(3x-6)}$

---

28. $f(x) = \dfrac{x^2 + 1}{x^2}$

29. $f(x) = \dfrac{-2x}{6 - 2x}$

_____

_____

30. $f(x) = \dfrac{-11}{4 + x}$

_____

Find the domain of the functions in problems 31-35; express each in interval notation.

31. $f(x) = x^3 + 4x^2 + 4x$

32. $f(x) = |2x - 1|$

_____

_____

33. $f(x) = \dfrac{8}{5x - 14}$

34. $f(x) = \dfrac{x^3 - |x|}{x^3 - 1}$

_____

_____

35. $f(x) = \dfrac{x^2 - 1}{x(x - 3)}$

_____

For problems 36-40, note whether or not each graph given represents a function.

36.
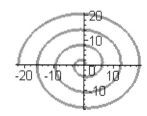

37.
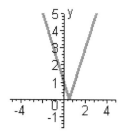

_____

_____

38.
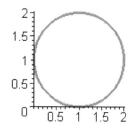

39.
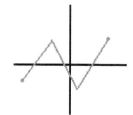

_____

_____

36

40.

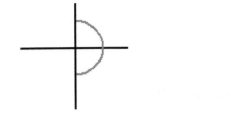

_____

Given function g graphed in the diagram below, answer questions 41-43.

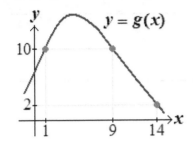

41. $g(1) = ?$ _____

42. $g(9) = ?$ _____

43. $g(14) = ?$ _____

Given function g graphed in the diagram below, answer questions 44-45.

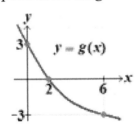

44. For what values of x does $g(x) = 3$? _____

45. For what values of x does $g(x) = 0$? _____

For problems 46 and 47 below, find: **a.** $f + g$ **d.** $\dfrac{f}{g}$

  b. $f - g$ **e.** $5g$

  c. $f \cdot g$ **f.** $5f$

Also, evaluate each function at $x = 7$.

46. $f(x) = x + 3$ and $g(x) = \dfrac{1}{2}x - 3$

a _____ _____

b _____ _____

c _____ _____

d _____ _____

e _____ _____

f _____ _____

47. $f(x) = x^2$ and $g(x) = 4x + 5$

a _____ _____

b _____ _____

c _____ _____

d _____ _____

e _____ _____

f _____ _____

Problems

Find the slope and y-intercept of the line depicted in the graph, for problems 1-8.

1.

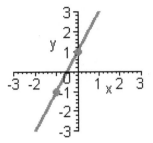

_____

2.

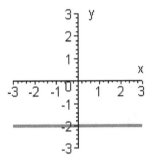

_____

3.

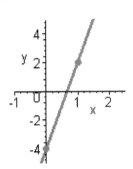

_____

4.

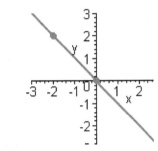

_____

5.

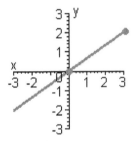

_____

6.

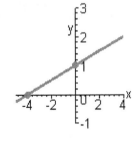

_____

7.

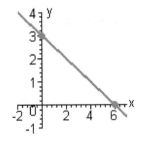

_____

8.

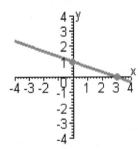

_____

For problems 9-22, find the slope of the line containing the given points.

9.   (1,3) and (3,1)

_____

10.   (3,–2) and (1,4)

_____

11.   (–1,–2) and (–3,2)

_____

12.   (0,3) and (4,0)

_____

13.   (2,4) and (2,–2)

_____

14.   (2,5) and (–3,–2)

_____

15.   (0,4) and (–2,5)

_____

16.   (3,–1) and (5,–1)

_____

17.   (4,1) and (4,–3)

_____

18.   (–2,–5) and (–4,–1)

_____

19.   (6,1) and (8,1)

_____

20.   (0,–3) and (–2,0)

_____

21.   (1,–2) and (–6,8)

_____

22.   (9,0) and (6,–2)

_____

For problems 23-40, find the slope and the y–intercept of the line with the given equation.

23. $y = 2x$

_____

24. $y = -x - 3$

_____

25. $y = 7x - 4$

_____

26. $2y + 25 = 12x - 1$

_____

27. $7(y - 2x) = -7x - 35$

28. $5y + 4x = 25$

_____

29. $5y = 7x - 27$

30. $y + x = 6$

_____

31. $y = -3$

32. $3y - 2x = 4$

_____

33. $f(x) = x + 7$

34. $y - 7 = -\dfrac{3}{2}x$

_____

35. $\dfrac{8}{3}y = -x - \dfrac{8}{15}$

36. $x = -4$

_____

37. $6x - 5y = 20$

38. $3x + 2y = 8$

_____

39. $5x = \dfrac{2}{3}y - 10$

40. $3 - \dfrac{1}{4}y = 2x$

_____

Chapter 2 Section 4: Equations of Lines

Problems

For problems 1-12, put your answers into slope–intercept form.

1. Find the equation of the line with slope -1, and passing through the point (2,0).

_____

2. Find the equation of the line with slope 4, and passing through the point (2, −3).

_____

3. Find the equation of the line with slope $\dfrac{1}{2}$, and passing through the point (0,2).

_____

4. Find the equation of the line with slope $\dfrac{4}{3}$, and passing through the point (−1,−3).

_____

5. Find the equation of the line with slope $\dfrac{5}{4}$, and passing through the point (−2,−3).

_____

6. Find the equation of the line with slope −3, and passing through the point (3, 0).

_____

7. Find the equation of the line with slope $\dfrac{3}{4}$, and passing through the point (4, 3).

_____

8. Find the equation of the line with slope $\dfrac{7}{5}$, and passing through the point (1,−4).

_____

9. Find the equation of the line with slope 3, and passing through the point (−3, 5).

_____

10. Find the equation of the line with slope 0, and passing through the point (−3,−2).

_____

11. Find the equation of the line with undefined slope, and passing through the point (−5,−1).

_____

12. Find the equation of the line with slope $-\dfrac{2}{3}$, and passing through the point (−3,−2).

_____

Find the equation of the line passing through the given points, for problems 13-20.

13. (0,2) and (3,5)

14. (−3,−5) and (4,−5)

15. (2,3) and (5,5)

16. (−1,−2) and (3,4)

17. (−2,−3) and (−1,−2)

18. (−2,5) and (−2,−5)

19. (0,4) and (2,0)

20. (3,1) and (−3,−6)

21. Find the equation of the line parallel to $2x - 3y = 2$ and passing through (−2,−4).

22. Find the equation of the line parallel to $y = 2x + 15$ and passing through (3,1) .

23. Find the equation of the line parallel to $2x + 5y = 1$ and passing through (0,0) .

24. Find the equation of the line parallel to $2x + 3y = 5$ and passing through (−1,4) .

25. Find the equation of the line parallel to $y = -6x$ and passing through (−1,5).

26. Find the equation of the line parallel to $x = -6$ and passing through (4,−2).

27. Find the equation of the line perpendicular to $2x - 5y = 10$ and passing through (−4,−3).

28. Find the equation of the line perpendicular to $x - 4y = 3$ and passing through (−2, 2) .

29. Find the equation of the line perpendicular to $y = \dfrac{1}{3}x - 3$ and passing through (4,1) .

30. Find the equation of the line perpendicular to $-3x - 5y = 2$ and passing through (2,−6).

31. Find the equation of the line perpendicular to $y = -3x + 4$ and passing through $(-4, -1)$.

32. Find the equation of the line perpendicular to $y = \frac{5}{2}x - 4$ and passing through $(2, -5)$.

_____

33. Graph the line $y = \frac{1}{2}x + 2$ using only the line's slope and y–intercept.

34. Graph the line $y = \frac{2}{3}x - 3$ using only the line's slope and y–intercept.

_____

35. Graph the line $3x + 2y = 6$ using only the line's x and y–intercepts.

36. Graph the line $x + y = 2$ using only the line's x and y–intercepts.

_____

37. Graph the line $2x + 3y = 6$ using only the line's x and y–intercepts.

_____

Find the equation of the graphed line, for problems 38-40.

38.

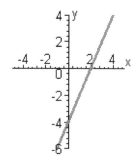

39.

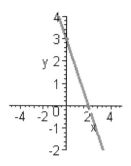

_____

_____

40.

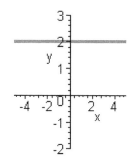

_____

Problems

Graph the solution set of each inequality.

1. $x + y \leq 4$

2. $2x + y < 5$

_____

_____

3. $x + 3y > -3$

4. $x - 2y \geq 2$

_____

_____

5. $2y + 3x \leq 15$

6. $3x - 4y \leq 12$

_____

_____

7. $8x + 3y < 24$

8. $5x + 6y \leq 30$

_____

_____

9. $7x - 4y > 28$

10. $3x - 5y > 15$

_____

_____

11. $-x + 2y > -8$

12. $\dfrac{x}{3} + \dfrac{y}{4} < 1$

_____

_____

13. $y \geq x + 1$

14. $y > -2x + 3$

_____

_____

15. $y < 2x$

16. $y \leq \dfrac{1}{2}x$

_____

17. $y > -\dfrac{2}{3}x + 3$

18. $y > \dfrac{3}{2}x + 3$

_____

19. $y \geq \dfrac{5}{2}x + 5$

20. $2x - 12 \geq 8y$

_____

21. $15 + 2y \leq 3x$

22. $6x + 3 > 3y$

_____

_____

23. $5y < 2x - 20$

24. $3x + 4 \geq 2y$

_____

_____

25. $12x > 2y + 9$

26. $9x \leq 12 - 3y$

_____

_____

27. $15 + 6y \geq 2x$

28. $\dfrac{2x - 3y}{6} > -\dfrac{2}{3}$

_____

_____

29. $1.5 \leq 0.3x - 0.5y$

30. $1.2 > 0.2x + 0.6y$

_____

_____

31. $y \leq -4$

32. $y > 0$

_____

_____

33. $x > -7$

34. $y \leq 8$

35. $y > -\dfrac{1}{3}$

36. $x < \dfrac{1}{2}$

37. $x \leq \dfrac{5}{8}$

38. $y \geq -\dfrac{13}{12}$

39. $x \geq -\dfrac{4}{3}$

40. $y > -1$

Intermediate algebra 2ND Edition
Practice Problem Worksheets

Chapter 3: Systems of Linear Equations

Chapter 3 Section 1: Substitution and Elimination

Problems

Solve the linear systems in problems 1-10 using substitution.

1. $y = 2x - 3$
    $y = 6x + 5$

    _____

2. $y = 7x - 9$
    $y = 3x - 5$

    _____

3. $y = 3x + 10$
    $y = 5x - 2$

    _____

4. $y = 2x - 3$
    $2x - 5y = 11$

    _____

5. $y = 7x - 1$
    $3x + 5y = -5$

    _____

6. $y = 2x + 7$
    $x + 3y = 14$

    _____

7. $y = 11 - 3x$
    $6x + 2y = 5$

    _____

8. $x = 4y + 6$
    $2x + 3y = 12$

    _____

9. $x = 6y - 2$
    $3x - y = 11$

    _____

10. $x = 5y - 1$
    $2x - 10y = -2$

    _____

Solve the linear systems in problems 11-40 using elimination.

11. $y - 5x = 1$
    $5x + 2y = -10$

    _____

12. $7x - 2y = 3$
    $7x + 2y = -1$

    _____

13. $5x + 4y = 7$
    $3x + 4y = 9$

    _____

14. $2x + 8y = 3$
    $6x + 8y = 7$

    _____

15. $4x = 1 + 9y$
$2x + 9y = -7$

16. $2x = 5 - 5y$
$6x - 5y = 1$

_____

_____

17. $10x = 1 - 6y$
$3 - 2y = 10x$

18. $2y - 4x = 3$
$7y + 2x = 1$

_____

_____

19. $x + 2y = 4$
$3x + 5y = 7$

20. $x - 4y = 7$
$3x - 12y = 10$

_____

_____

21. $3x - 8y = 1$
$12x - 5y = 4$

22. $10x - 2y = 3$
$11x + 3y = 2$

_____

_____

23. $7x + 5y = 2$
$2x - 3y = 5$

24. $21x - 14y = 7$
$-3x + 2y = -1$

_____

_____

25. $20x - 4y = 1$
$-2x + 8y = -1$

26. $14x - 2y = 1$
$5x + 4y = 4$

_____

_____

27. $6x - 7y = 4$
$-18x + 21y = 12$

28. $2x - 9y = 5$
$-3x + 4y = -7$

_____

_____

29. $4x = 12y - 9$
$-2x + 7y = 1$

30. $3x = 13y - 10$
$-3x + 14y = 2$

_____

_____

31. $3(2x - y) = 2(3y - x)$
$4(x + y) = 3(y - 3x)$

_____

32. $2(2x - 1) = 3(2y - x)$
$5(x + y) = -(y - 2)$

_____

33. $3(x - 1) - 1 = 3(5y + x)$
$2(x - 3y) = -(y + 3) + 1$

_____

34. $2(2x + 3) + 2 = 3(y - 1)$
$9y - 4x = 8(x + 1)$

_____

35. $\dfrac{x}{2} - \dfrac{2y}{3} = \dfrac{5}{6}$

$\dfrac{5x}{6} + \dfrac{y}{3} = \dfrac{1}{2}$

_____

36. $\dfrac{x}{3} - \dfrac{2y}{5} = \dfrac{4}{15}$

$\dfrac{3x}{2} - \dfrac{y}{5} = \dfrac{2}{5}$

_____

37. $\dfrac{x}{6} - 2y = \dfrac{5}{3}$

$3x - \dfrac{y}{2} = \dfrac{5}{2}$

_____

38. $\dfrac{x}{2} + 2y = \dfrac{3}{5}$

$2x - \dfrac{y}{4} = \dfrac{3}{2}$

_____

39. $\dfrac{x}{3} + 3y = \dfrac{1}{3}$

$3x - \dfrac{y}{3} = \dfrac{2}{3}$

_____

40. $\dfrac{x}{2} + 15y = \dfrac{5}{4}$

$4x - \dfrac{y}{3} = \dfrac{1}{2}$

_____

Chapter 3 Section 2: Applications of Linear Systems with Two Variables

Problems

1. Suppose you have 51 coins consisting of nickels and quarters, worth a total of $7.15. How many nickels and quarters do you have?

    _____

2. A jar contains 57 coins consisting of nickels and dimes, worth a total of $4.15. How many nickels and dimes are in the jar?

    _____

3. Julie's purse contains 37 coins consisting of nickels and quarters, worth a total of $5.25. How many nickels and quarters does she have?

    _____

4. Suppose you have 55 coins consisting of pennies and nickels, worth a total of $1.63. How many pennies and nickels do you have?

    _____

5. You have 168 coins consisting of pennies and dimes, worth a total of $5.82. How many pennies and dimes do you have?

    _____

6. A purse contains 232 coins consisting of nickels and quarters, worth a total of $20.40. How many nickels and quarters are in the purse?

    _____

7. A jar contains 87 coins consisting of dimes and quarters, worth a total of $14.55. How many dimes and quarters are in the jar?

    _____

8. You have 175 coins consisting of pennies and dimes, worth a total of $8.50. How many pennies and dimes do you have?

    _____

9.   A jar contains 317 coins consisting of pennies and quarters, worth a total of $13.25. How many pennies and quarters are in the jar?

           _____

10.   A purse contains 177 coins consisting of nickels and quarters, worth a total of $24.45. How many nickels and quarters are in the purse?

           _____

11.   Suppose you need to mix some 20% alcohol solution, and some 60% alcohol solution, to end up with 8 liters of 45% solution. How much of each solution should you use?

           _____

12.   Mara needs to mix some 30% acid solution, and some 70% alcohol solution, to end up with 15 liters of 54% solution. How much of each solution should she mix?

           _____

13.   Joshua must mix some 25% alcohol solution and some 75% alcohol solution, to end up with 16 quarts of 37.5% alcohol solution. How much of each solution should he use?

           _____

14.   Suppose you must mix some 40% acid solution, and some 80% acid solution, to end up with 20 gallons of 70% acid solution. How much of each solution should you use?

           _____

15.   Suppose you need to mix some 50% alcohol solution, and some 75% alcohol solution, to end up with 14 liters of 60% solution. How much of each solution should you use?

           _____

16.   One serving of soybeans contains 14 grams of protein and 8 grams of fat. One serving of rice contains 4 grams of protein and 1/2 gram of fat. How many servings of each should you combine, if you want to end up with precisely 20 grams of protein and 10 grams of fat?

           _____

17.   One serving of salmon contains 140 calories and 21 grams of protein. One serving of rice contains 230 calories and 5 grams of protein. How many servings of each should you combine, to end up with 300 calories and 25 grams of protein? (Round your answer to the nearest tenth of a serving.)

           _____

18. One serving of broccoli contains 50 calories and 10 grams of carbohydrates. One serving of rice contains 230 calories and 50 grams of carbohydrates. How many servings of each should you combine, if you want to end up with precisely 300 calories and 64 grams of carbohydrates?

_____

19. One serving of broccoli contains 50 calories and 5 grams of protein. One serving of salmon contains 140 calories and 21 grams of protein. How many servings of each should you combine, if you want to end up with precisely 300 calories and 35 grams of protein? (Round your answer to the nearest tenth of a serving.)

_____

20. One serving of tofu contains 9 grams of protein and 85 calories. One serving of rice contains 4 grams of protein and 230 calories. How many servings of each should you combine, if you want to end up with precisely 15 grams of protein and 300 calories? (Round your answer to the nearest tenth of a serving.)

_____

21. Josh invests $4,000 into two accounts. One account earns 8% interest and the other earns 12% interest. After one year his total interest earned from the two accounts totals $380. How much did Josh invest into each of the accounts?

_____

22. You invest $7,000 into two accounts. One account earns 6% interest and the other earns 15% interest. After one year your total interest earned from the two accounts is $600. How much did you invest into each of the accounts?

_____

23. A total of $23,000 is invested into two accounts. One account earns 7% interest and the other earns 11% interest. After one year the total interest earned from the two accounts totals $2,130. How much was invested into each of the accounts?

_____

24. Marsha invests $11,000 into two accounts. One account earns 8% interest and the other earns 14% interest. After one year her total interest earned from the two accounts totals $1,384. How much did Marsha invest into each of the accounts?

_____

25. A total of $9,000 is invested in two accounts. One account earns 5% interest and the other earns 20% interest. After one year the total interest earned from the two accounts is $1,320. How much was invested into each of the accounts?

_____

26. Paul can motorboat downstream a distance of 24 miles in two hours. Going upstream, it takes him 4 hours to motorboat the same distance. How fast could the motorboat go if there were no current, and what is the speed of the current?

    _____

27. Diane can kayak downstream a distance of 36 kilometers in two hours. Going upstream, in three hours she can only kayak a distance of 24 kilometers. How fast would the kayak go in still water, and how fast is the current?

    _____

28. Zenda can row downstream a distance of 30 kilometers in three hours. Going upstream, it takes her 4 hours to row only 8 kilometers. How fast could Zenda row in still water, and how fast is the current?

    _____

29. Ananda can kayak downstream a distance of 14 miles in two hours. Going upstream, in 5 hours he can kayak a distance of 15 miles. How fast could Ananda kayak if there were no current, and what is the speed of the current?

    _____

30. Nori can motorboat downstream a distance of 81 kilometers in three hours. Going upstream, in 4 hours she can boat 52 kilometers. How fast could the boat go in still water, and how fast is the current?

    _____

31. A plane flies 1,590 miles in 3 hours, with the wind. On its return trip, it took 4 hours flying against the same wind to go 1,480 miles. How fast would the plane have flown without any wind?

    _____

32. An airliner flies 3,240 miles in 4 hours with the wind. On its return trip, it took 5 hours flying against the same wind to go 3,150 miles. What was the wind speed?

    _____

33. An airliner flies 3,040 miles in 4 hours with the wind. On its return trip, it took 5 hours flying against the same wind to go 3,000 miles. How fast would the airliner have flown without any wind.

    _____

34. A plane flies 580 miles in 2 hours with the wind. On its return trip, it took 3 hours flying against the same wind to go 570 miles. What was the speed of the wind?

    _____

35. A plane flies 2,200 kilometers in 4 hours with the wind. On its return trip, it took 4.5 hours flying against the same wind to go 2,115 kilometers. How fast would the plane have flown without any wind?

    _____

36. Two types of tickets are sold for a film. Adult tickets cost $7 each, while a child's ticket costs $4. A total of 95 tickets are sold, bringing in a total of $620. How many of each type of ticket were sold?

    _____

37. Two types of tickets are sold for a concert. Adult tickets cost $8 each, while a child's ticket costs $3. A total of 150 tickets are sold, bringing in a total of $1,050. How many of each type of ticket were sold?

    _____

38. Two types of tickets are sold for a benefit concert. Adult tickets cost $10 each, while a child's ticket costs $6. A total of 240 tickets are sold, bringing in a total of $2,240. How many of each type of ticket were sold?

    _____

39. Two types of tickets are sold for a concert. Adult tickets cost $11 each, while student tickets each cost $7. A total of 330 tickets are sold, bringing in a total of $3,150. How many of each type of ticket were sold?

    _____

40. Two types of tickets are sold for a concert. Adult tickets cost $12 each, while student tickets each cost $8. A total of 270 tickets are sold, bringing in a total of $2,800. How many of each type of ticket were sold?

    _____

Problems

Solve.

1. Solve for x: $\begin{vmatrix} x & -3 \\ 3 & 18 \end{vmatrix} = 27$

2. Solve for x: $\begin{vmatrix} 4 & -x \\ 2 & 5 \end{vmatrix} = 30$

---

3. Solve for y: $\begin{vmatrix} 10 & 5 \\ 2y & -1 \end{vmatrix} = -100$

4. Solve for y: $\begin{vmatrix} 6 & 5 \\ y & y \end{vmatrix} = 13$

---

5. Solve for z: $\begin{vmatrix} z & z \\ 10 & 5 \end{vmatrix} = -35$

6. Solve for z: $\begin{vmatrix} 2z & -1 \\ z & -2 \end{vmatrix} = -9$

Solve each linear system, if possible. When there is no unique solution, state whether the system is inconsistent or dependent.

7.
$$x + 2y = 7$$
$$3x + 5y = 4$$

8.
$$x - 3y = 4$$
$$3x + 4y = 1$$

9.
$$x + 7y = 8$$
$$2x - 3y = 5$$

10.
$$2x - 5y = 10$$
$$4x - 3y = 12$$

11.
$$x + 8y = 3$$
$$2x + 9y = 5$$

12.
$$-x + 8y = -4$$
$$2x - 16y = 8$$

13.
$$2x + 6y = 11$$
$$4x - 8y = 13$$

14.
$$2x - 9y = 1$$
$$9x + 2y = 1$$

15.
$$-5x + 2y = -1$$
$$15x - 6y = 4$$

16.
$$5x + 3y = 2$$
$$15x + 5y = 6$$

---

17. $4x - y = 0$

$6x + 5y = 1$

_____

18. $8x + 3y = 2$

$4x - 6y = 1$

_____

19. $2x - 7y = -9$

$8x - 5y = 11$

_____

20. $3x + 6y = -2$

$6x + 4y = -1$

_____

21. $5x + 3y = 2$

$2x - 3y = 5$

_____

22. $2x - y = 1$

$-10x + 5y = 1$

_____

23. $2x - 11y = 1$

$7x + y = -1$

_____

24. $x - 5y - 2z = 1$

$2x - y + 2z = 0$

$2x - 3y - z = 0$

_____

25. $-5x + y - 3z = 1$

$5x - 2y + 2z = 0$

$-15x + 5y - 2z = 6$

_____

26. $x + y - 2z = 1$

$8x - 3y + 2z = -4$

$3x + 4y - z = 12$

_____

27. $-2x + y + 3z = -2$

$6x - 3y + 2z = 1$

$4x - 2y - 6z = 4$

_____

28. $-2x + y + z = 2$

$6x - 2y + 3z = 1$

$2x + y - 2z = -1$

_____

29. $-x + 2y - z = 3$

$3x - 8y + 2z = -1$

$9x + 5y - 3z = 0$

_____

30. $2x + y - 2z = 3$

$6x - y + 2z = 1$

$4x + 3y - z = 1$

_____

31.
$-x - 3y + 2z = 4$
$2x - 3z = 5$
$5x + 15y - 10z = 6$

_____

32.
$3x + y - 2z = 0$
$6x - 3z = 1$
$21x - 3y - z = 1$

_____

33.
$x - 3y - z = 4$
$-4x - y = 4$
$3x + 2y - 3z = 0$

_____

34.
$x + 2y - 2z = 1$
$-3y + 3z = -1$
$6x + 3y - 11z = 0$

_____

35.
$x - 4y + z = 1$
$2x + z = 1$
$3x - 2y - z = 1$

_____

36.
$2x + 3y - z = 0$
$6x - 5y = 4$
$12x + y = 0$

_____

37.
$2x - y + 3z = 1$
$4x - 2y + 6z = 1$
$-4x + 2y - 3z = 0$

_____

38.
$2x - y + 5z = 1$
$4x - y + z = 1$
$-4x + 2y - 3z = 0$

_____

39.
$5x - 2y + z = 1$
$30x + 3y - 2z = 0$ Then $z = ?$
$45x - y + 4z = 0$

_____

40.
$4x - y + 3z = 1$
$-4x + y - z = 1$ Then $z = ?$
$24x - 2y + 3z = 0$

_____

41.
$\dfrac{x}{2} - y + \dfrac{z}{2} = 0$

$-2x + \dfrac{y}{3} + z = -\dfrac{2}{3}$ Then $y = ?$

$x - 2y + \dfrac{z}{2} = 1$

_____

42.
$\dfrac{x}{3} - y + \dfrac{z}{2} = \dfrac{1}{6}$

$-x + \dfrac{y + 3z}{2} = 1$ Then $y = ?$

$x - y + \dfrac{z}{3} = 1$

_____

43.

$$\frac{x}{2} + \frac{y}{10} + \frac{z}{5} = \frac{1}{10}$$

$$2x - \frac{y + 2z}{2} = 1 \qquad \text{Then } z = ?$$

$$x + 2y + \frac{z}{5} = 1$$

44.

$$\frac{5x}{6} + \frac{y}{2} - \frac{z}{3} = 1$$

$$-x + \frac{y}{2} = \frac{1}{2} \qquad \text{Then } z = ?$$

$$-y + \frac{z}{5} = 1$$

45.

$$0.3x + 0.2y + 0.5z = 1$$

$$1.2x - y - 0.6z = 0 \qquad \text{Then } x = ?$$

$$0.4y + 0.6z = 0.5$$

46.

$$0.01x + 0.02y - 0.03z = 0$$

$$2.2x - 1.4y + 0.8z = 1 \qquad \text{Then } x = ?$$

$$0.02y - 0.08z = 0.04$$

Problems

Solve each linear system, if possible. When there is no unique solution, state whether the system is inconsistent or dependent.

1. $x + 2y = 7$
$3x + 5y = 4$

2. $x - 3y = 19$
$3x + 4y = -8$

---

3. $x + 7y = 20$
$2x - 3y = 6$

4. $2x - 5y = 23$
$4x - 3y = 25$

---

5. $x + 8y = 3$
$2x + 9y = 5$

6. $-x + 8y = -4$
$2x - 16y = 8$

---

7. $2x + 6y = 4$
$4x - 8y = -12$

8. $2x - 9y = 40$
$9x + 2y = 10$

---

9. $-5x + 2y = -1$
$15x - 6y = 4$

10. $5x + 3y = 2$
$15x + 5y = 6$

---

11. $4x - y = 0$
$6x + 5y = 1$

12. $8x + 3y = 2$
$4x - 6y = 1$

---

13. $2x - 7y = -9$
$8x - 5y = 11$

14. $3x + 6y = 4$
$6x + 4y = 4$

---

15. $5x + 3y = 2$
$2x - 3y = 5$

16. $2x - y = 1$
$-10x + 5y = 1$

---

17. $2x - 11y = 1$
$7x + y = -1$

18. $x - 5y - 2z = -8$
$2x - y + 2z = 5$
$2x - 3y - z = -3$

19.
$$-5x + y - 3z = 1$$
$$5x - 2y + 2z = 0$$
$$-15x + 5y - 2z = -6$$

20.
$$x + y - 2z = 3$$
$$8x - 3y + 2z = 20$$
$$3x + 4y - z = 16$$

21.
$$-2x + y + 3z = -2$$
$$6x - 3y + 2z = 1$$
$$4x - 2y - 6z = 4$$

22.
$$-2x + y + z = 2$$
$$6x - 2y + 3z = 1$$
$$2x + y - 2z = -1$$

23.
$$-x + 2y - z = 1$$
$$3x - 8y + 2z = -9$$
$$9x + 5y - 3z = 13$$

24.
$$2x + y - 2z = 3$$
$$6x - y + 2z = 1$$
$$4x + 3y - z = 1$$

25.
$$3x + y - 2z = 0$$
$$6x - 3z = 1$$
$$21x - 3y - z = 1$$

26.
$$-x - 3y + 2z = 4$$
$$2x - 3z = 5$$
$$5x + 15y - 10z = 6$$

27.
$$x - 3y - z = 4$$
$$-4x - y = 4$$
$$3x + 2y - 3z = 0$$

28.
$$x + 2y - 2z = 6$$
$$-3y + 3z = -6$$
$$6x + 3y - 11z = 42$$

29.
$$x - 4y + z = 1$$
$$2x + z = 1$$
$$3x - 2y - z = 1$$

30.
$$2x + 3y - z = 13$$
$$6x - 5y = 20$$
$$12x + y = 62$$

31.
$$2x - y + 3z = 1$$
$$4x - 2y + 6z = 1$$
$$-4x + 2y - 3z = 0$$

32.
$$2x - y + 5z = 1$$
$$4x - y + z = 1$$
$$-4x + 2y - 3z = 0$$

33.
$$5x - 2y + z = -3$$
$$30x + 3y - 2z = 4$$
$$45x - y + 4z = 2$$

_____

34.
$$4x - y + 3z = 11$$
$$-4x + y - z = -17$$
$$24x - 2y + 3z = 111$$

_____

35.
$$\frac{x}{2} - y + \frac{z}{2} = 0$$
$$-2x + \frac{y}{3} + z = -\frac{2}{3}$$
$$x - 2y + \frac{z}{2} = 1$$

_____

36.
$$\frac{x}{3} - y + \frac{z}{2} = \frac{2}{3}$$
$$-x + \frac{y}{2} + \frac{3z}{2} = \frac{3}{2}$$
$$x - y + \frac{z}{3} = \frac{5}{3}$$

_____

37.
$$\frac{x}{2} + \frac{y}{10} + \frac{z}{5} = \frac{9}{10}$$
$$2x - \frac{y}{2} - z = 0$$
$$x + 2y + \frac{z}{5} = \frac{7}{5}$$

_____

38.
$$\frac{5x}{6} + \frac{y}{2} - \frac{z}{3} = \frac{5}{3}$$
$$-x + \frac{y}{2} = -\frac{7}{2}$$
$$-y + \frac{z}{5} = \frac{6}{5}$$

_____

39.
$$0.3x + 0.2y + 0.5z = 1$$
$$1.2x - y - 0.6z = 0$$
$$0.4y + 0.6z = 0.5$$

_____

40.
$$0.01x + 0.02y - 0.03z = -0.01$$
$$2.2x - 1.4y + 0.8z = 6.8$$
$$0.02y - 0.08z = -0.14$$

_____

Problems

1. You find 17 coins consisting only of nickels, dimes, and quarters, with a face value of $2.75. However, the coins all date from 1929, and are worth considerably more than their face value. A coin dealer offers you $7 for each nickel, $5 for each dime, and $20 for each quarter, for a total of $211. How many of each type of coin did you find?

   _____

2. You find 32 coins consisting only of nickels, dimes, and quarters, with a face value of $3.75. However, the coins all date from 1929, and are worth considerably more than their face value. A coin dealer offers you $7 for each nickel, $5 for each dime, and $20 for each quarter, for a total of $285. How many of each type of coin did you find?

   _____

3. You find 56 coins consisting only of nickels, dimes, and quarters, with a face value of $7.50. However, the coins all date from 1929, and are worth considerably more than their face value. A coin dealer offers you $12 for each nickel, $9 for each dime, and $18 for each quarter, for a total of $714. How many of each type of coin did you find?

   _____

4. You find 50 coins consisting only of nickels, dimes, and quarters, with a face value of $8.25. However, the coins all date from 1929, and are worth considerably more than their face value. A coin dealer offers you $12 for each nickel, $9 for each dime, and $18 for each quarter, for a total of $705. How many of each type of coin did you find?

   _____

5. A bag of 105 coins consist only of nickels, dimes, and quarters, with a face value of $14.25. The number of nickels and dimes together exceeds the number of quarters by 35. How many of each type of coin are in the bag?

   _____

6. A jar of 47 coins consist only of nickels, dimes, and quarters, with a face value of $5.00. The number of nickels and dimes together exceeds the number of quarters by 33. How many of each type of coin are in the bag?

   _____

7. A bag of 130 coins consist only of pennies, nickels, and dimes, with a face value of $4.75. There are 10 more pennies than the total number of nickels and dimes together. How many of each type of coin are in the bag?

   _____

8. A jar of 500 coins consist only of pennies, nickels, and dimes, with a face value of $22.50. The number of pennies equals the sum of the numbers of nickels and dimes. How many of each type of coin are in the bag?

    _____

9. A nutritionist needs to calculate the number of servings of brown rice, broccoli, and tofu, to create a meal containing 500 calories, 33 grams of protein, and 13 grams of fat. The nutritional content of one serving of these foods is given in the following table:

	Calories	Protein	Fat
Rice	230	5	1
Broccoli	50	5	1
Tofu	85	9	5

    How many servings of each food should be combined?

    _____

10. A nutritionist needs to calculate the number of servings of brown rice, broccoli, and tofu, to create a meal containing 680 calories, 33 grams of protein, and 13 grams of fat. The nutritional content of one serving of these foods is given in the following table:

	Calories	Protein	Fat
Rice	230	5	1
Broccoli	50	5	1
Tofu	85	9	5

    How many servings of each food should be combined?

    _____

11. A nutritionist needs to calculate the number of servings of brown rice, broccoli, and salmon, to create a meal containing 508 calories, 39 grams of protein, and 11 grams of fat. The nutritional content of one serving of these foods is given in the following table:

	Calories	Protein	Fat
Rice	230	5	1
Broccoli	50	5	1
Salmon	178	24	8

    How many servings of each food should be combined?

    _____

12. A nutritionist needs to calculate the number of servings of brown rice, broccoli, and salmon, to create a meal containing 866 calories, 63 grams of protein, and 19 grams of fat. The nutritional content of one serving of these foods is given in the following table:

	Calories	Protein	Fat
Rice	230	5	1
Broccoli	50	5	1
Salmon	178	24	8

How many servings of each food should be combined?

_____

13. A factory has three machines capable of producing baseball bats. All three machines together can produce 190 baseball bats per hour. Machine A and machine B together can produce 155 baseball bats per hour, while machine A and machine C can together produce 90 baseball bats per hour. How many baseball bats per hour can each machine produce?

_____

14. A factory has three machines capable of producing keyboards. All three machines together can produce 565 keyboards per hour. Machine A and machine B together can produce 365 keyboards per hour, while machine A and machine C can together produce 265 keyboards per hour. How many keyboards per hour can each machine produce?

_____

15. A factory has three workers capable of producing pens. All three workers together can produce 1150 pens per hour. Worker A and worker B together can produce 540 pens per hour, while worker A and worker C can together produce 800 pens per hour. How many pens per hour can each worker produce?

_____

16. A mint has three machines capable of making coins. All three machines together can make 140 coins per minute. Machine A and machine B together can produce 100 coins per minute, while machine A and machine C can together produce 80 coins per minute. How many coins per minute can each machine make?

_____

17. A mint has three machines capable of making coins. All three machines together can make 212 coins per minute. Machine A is twice as fast as machine B. Machine C can make 12 less coins per minute than machine B. How many coins per minute can each machine make?

    _____

18. A factory has three machines capable of making cups. All three machines together can make 210 cups per minute. Machine A can produce 50 more cups per minute than machine B. Machine C can make 10 more cups per minute than machine B. How many cups per minute can each machine make?

    _____

19. Jay and Sarah can assemble 66 bead strands in 30 minutes. Mikey and Sarah can assemble 78 strands in 30 minutes. Working together, all three can assemble 118 strands in 30 minutes. How many strands can each person assemble in 30 minutes?

    _____

20. Bill, Pat, and Doug can build 29 robots per week. If Bill can build 3 more robots per week than Doug, and Pat can build 1 less robot per week than Doug, how many robots can each person build in a week?

    _____

21. Three kinds of tickets were sold for a concert. Child tickets cost $5, adult tickets cost $15, and student tickets cost $10. A total of 90 tickets were sold, bringing in a total of $1,000. If the number of student tickets sold was one-and-a-half times the number of child tickets sold, how many tickets of each type were sold?

    _____

22. Three kinds of tickets were sold for a concert. Child tickets cost $6, adult tickets cost $18, and student tickets cost $9. A total of 100 tickets were sold, bringing in a total of $1,260. If the number of adult tickets sold equaled the total number of student and child tickets combined, how many tickets of each type were sold?

    _____

23. Three kinds of tickets were sold for a concert. Child tickets cost $5, adult tickets cost $20, and student tickets cost $10. A total of 180 tickets were sold, bringing in a total of $2,700. If 20 more adult tickets were sold than the total number of student and child tickets combined, how many tickets of each type were sold?

   _____

24. Three kinds of tickets were sold for a concert. Child tickets cost $6, adult tickets cost $12, and student tickets cost $8. A total of 80 tickets were sold, bringing in a total of $796. If 10 more adult tickets were sold than the total number of student and child tickets combined, how many tickets of each type were sold?

   _____

25. Three sizes of soft drink are sold at a festival. The large (24 oz) is sold for $3, the medium (16 oz) for $2, and the small (10 oz) for $1.50. 450 drinks are sold bringing in a total of $950. If a total of 7200 oz of soft drink was sold, how many of each size drink was sold?

   _____

26. Three sizes of soft drink are sold at a festival. The large (24 oz) is sold for $3, the medium (16 oz) for $2, and the small (10 oz) for $1.50. 240 drinks are sold bringing in a total of $510. If a total of 3880 oz of soft drink was sold, how many of each size drink was sold?

   _____

27. Three sizes of soft drink are sold at a festival. The large (24 oz) is sold for $3, the medium (16 oz) for $2.50, and the small (10 oz) for $2. 470 drinks are sold bringing in a total of $1160. If a total of 7580 oz of soft drink was sold, how many of each size drink was sold?

   _____

28. Three sizes of soft drink are sold at a festival. The large (24 oz) is sold for $3, the medium (16 oz) for $2.50, and the small (10 oz) for $2. 450 drinks are sold bringing in a total of $1100. If a total of 7200 oz of soft drink was sold, how many of each size drink was sold?

   _____

Chapter 3 Section 4: Applications of Linear Systems with Three Variables - Gaussian Elimination

Problems

1. You find 20 coins consisting only of nickels, dimes, and quarters, with a face value of $2.65. However, the coins all date from 1929, and are worth considerably more than their face value. A coin dealer offers you $7 for each nickel, $5 for each dime, and $20 for each quarter, for a total of $221. How many of each type of coin did you find?

    _____

2. You find 48 coins consisting only of nickels, dimes, and quarters, with a face value of $7.20. However, the coins all date from 1929, and are worth considerably more than their face value. A coin dealer offers you $7 for each nickel, $5 for each dime, and $20 for each quarter, for a total of $585. How many of each type of coin did you find?

    _____

3. You find 60 coins consisting only of nickels, dimes, and quarters, with a face value of $7.70. However, the coins all date from 1920, and are worth considerably more than their face value. A coin dealer offers you $12 for each nickel, $9 for each dime, and $18 for each quarter, for a total of $780. How many of each type of coin did you find?

    _____

4. You find 75 coins consisting only of nickels, dimes, and quarters, with a face value of $11.00. However, the coins all date from 1920, and are worth considerably more than their face value. A coin dealer offers you $12 for each nickel, $9 for each dime, and $18 for each quarter, for a total of $1,005. How many of each type of coin did you find?

    _____

5. A bag of 110 coins consists only of nickels, dimes, and quarters, with a face value of $16.75. The number of nickels and dimes together exceed the number of quarters by 10. How many of each type of coin are in the bag?

    _____

6. A jar of 60 coins consists only of nickels, dimes, and quarters, with a face value of $8.65. The number of nickels and dimes together exceed the number of quarters by 10. How many of each type of coin are in the jar?

    _____

7. A bag of 192 coins consists only of pennies, nickels, and dimes, with a face value of $7.62. There are 12 more pennies than the total number of nickels and dimes together. How many of each type of coin are in the bag?

_____

8. A jar of 400 coins consists only of pennies, nickels, and dimes, with a face value of $17. The number of pennies equals the sum of the numbers of nickels and dimes. How many of each type of coin are in the jar?

_____

9. A nutritionist needs to calculate the number of servings of brown rice, broccoli, and tofu, to create a meal containing 695 calories, 34 grams of protein, and 10 grams of fat. The nutritional content of one serving of these foods is given in the following table:

	Calories	Protein	Fat
Rice	230	5	1
Broccoli	50	5	1
Tofu	85	9	5

How many servings of each food should be combined?

_____

10. A nutritionist needs to calculate the number of servings of brown rice, broccoli, and tofu, to create a meal containing 415 calories, 24 grams of protein, and 8 grams of fat. The nutritional content of one serving of these foods is given in the following table:

	Calories	Protein	Fat
Rice	230	5	1
Broccoli	50	5	1
Tofu	85	9	5

How many servings of each food should be combined?

_____

11. A nutritionist needs to calculate the number of servings of brown rice, broccoli, and salmon, to create a meal containing 458 calories, 34 grams of protein, and 10 grams of fat. The nutritional content of one serving of these foods is given in the following table:

	Calories	Protein	Fat
Rice	230	5	1
Broccoli	50	5	1
Salmon	178	24	8

How many servings of each food should be combined?

_____

12. A nutritionist needs to calculate the number of servings of brown rice, broccoli, and salmon, to create a meal containing 738 calories, 44 grams of protein, and 12 grams of fat. The nutritional content of one serving of these foods is given in the following table:

	Calories	Protein	Fat
Rice	230	5	1
Broccoli	50	5	1
Salmon	178	24	8

How many servings of each food should be combined?

_____

13. A factory has three machines capable of producing cogs. All three machines together can produce 530 cogs per hour. Machine A and machine B together can produce 350 cogs per hour, while machine A and machine C can together produce 300 cogs per hour. How many cogs per hour can each machine produce?

_____

14. A factory has three machines capable of producing widgets. All three machines together can produce 200 widgets per hour. Machine A and machine B together can produce 130 widgets per hour, while machine A and machine C can together produce 150 widgets per hour. How many widgets per hour can each machine produce?

_____

15. A factory has three machines capable of producing ping-pong balls. All three machines together can produce 980 balls per hour. Machine A and machine B together can produce 650 balls per hour, while machine A and machine C can together produce 600 balls per hour. How many balls can each machine produce in one hour?

_____

16. A mint has three machines capable of making coins. All three machines together can make 160 coins per minute. Machine A and machine B together can make 100 coins per minute, while machine A and machine C can together make 110 coins per minute. How many coins per minute can each machine make?

_____

17. A mint has three machines capable of making coins. All three machines together can make 217 coins per minute. Machine A is twice as fast as machine B. Machine C can make 25 more coins per minute than machine B. How many coins per minute can each machine make?

_____

18. A factory has three machines capable of making cogs. All three machines together can make 300 cogs per minute. Machine A can produce 20 more cogs per minute than machine B. Machine C can make 10 more cogs per minute than machine B. How many cogs per minute can each machine make?

_____

19. Jon and Sky can assemble 64 bead strands in 30 minutes. Mara and Sky can assemble 50 strands in 30 minutes. Working all together, all three can assemble 80 strands in 30 minutes. How many strands can each person assemble in 30 minutes?

_____

20. Mary and Joe and Tom can build 27 robots per week. If Mary can build 5 more robots per week than Tom, and Joe can build 2 less robots per week than Tom, how many robots can each person build in a week?

_____

21. Three kinds of tickets were sold for a concert. Child tickets cost $5, adult tickets cost $15, and student tickets cost $10. A total of 128 tickets were sold, bringing in a total of $1,545. If the number of student tickets sold was three times the number of child tickets sold, how many tickets of each type were sold?

_____

22. Three kinds of tickets were sold for a concert. Child tickets cost $6, adult tickets cost $18, and student tickets cost $9. A total of 200 tickets were sold, bringing in a total of $2,640. If the number of adult tickets sold equaled the total number of student and child tickets combined, how many tickets of each type were sold?

_____

23. Three kinds of tickets were sold for a concert. Child tickets cost $5, adult tickets cost $20, and student tickets cost $10. A total of 220 tickets were sold, bringing in a total of $3,275. If 20 more adult tickets were sold than the total number of student and child tickets combined, how many tickets of each type were sold?

_____

24. Three kinds of tickets were sold for a concert. Child tickets are $6, adult tickets are $12, and student tickets are $8. A total of 187 tickets were sold, bringing in a total of $1,848. If 11 more adult tickets were sold than the total number of student and child tickets combined, how many tickets of each type were sold?

_____

25.   Three sizes of soft drink are sold at a festival. The large (24 oz) is sold for $3, the medium (16 oz) for $2, and the small (10 oz) for $1.50. 730 drinks are sold bringing in a total of $1,570. If a total of 12,000 oz of soft drink was sold, how many of each size drink was sold?

_____

26.   Three sizes of soft drink are sold at a concert. The large (24 oz) is sold for $3, the medium (16 oz) for $2, and the small (10 oz) for $1.50. 320 drinks are sold bringing in a total of $705. If a total of 5,420 oz of soft drink was sold, how many of each size drink was sold?

_____

27.   Three sizes of soft drink are sold at a benefit. The large (24 oz) is sold for $3, the medium (16 oz) for $2.50, and the small (10 oz) for $2. 440 drinks are sold bringing in a total of $1,120. If a total of 7,620 oz of soft drink was sold, how many of each size drink was sold?

_____

28.   Three sizes of soft drink are sold at a street fair. The large (24 oz) is sold for $3, the medium (16 oz) for $2.50, and the small (10 oz) for $2. 180 drinks are sold bringing in a total of $440. If a total of 2,860 oz of soft drink was sold, how many of each size drink was sold?

_____

Problems

Graph each system of linear inequalities.

1. $4x + y \leq 5$
$2x - y \geq 3$

2. $5x + 4y \leq 3$
$x - 3y < 2$

---

3. $2x - 3y > 9$
$7x - y < 1$

4. $7x + 9y < 0$
$x - 9y < 8$

---

5. $2x + 5y \leq 3$
$2x - 3y \geq 4$

6. $6x - 3y > 18$
$3x + 2y \geq 6$

---

7. $2x + y \leq 5$
       $3x - y < 5$

8. $5x + 3y > 5$
       $4x - 7y \geq -3$

9. $-2x + 5y > 10$
       $6x - 7y > -42$

10. $y - 2x \leq -3$
       $y \geq -x + 2$

11. $y - 7x > 2$
       $y \geq 3x + 1$

12. $y + 4x < 5$
       $y < x + 3$

13. $y - x \leq -2$
$y \geq -3x - 4$

14. $3y + 2x > -3$
$3y > -x + 2$

_____

_____

15. $y - 5x > 0$
$2y \geq 2x + 1$

16. $2x - 4y \geq -3$
$y \geq x - 5$

_____

_____

17. $3y - x \leq 6$
$6y \geq -x - 3$

18. $2y \leq x - 3$
$3y \geq -x + 4$

_____

_____

19. $2y - 3x \leq -6$
$3y \geq -2x + 6$

20. $5y - x < 10$
$y < 5x - 10$

_____

21. $2y - 2x \leq -3$
$y \geq -x + 1$
$y < 4$

22.* $3x + 2y < 6$
$x - 2y > 4$
$y > -6$

_____

23 $3x - y > -10$
$3x - y \leq 10$
$-4 < x < 4$

24. $5x - 2y \leq 10$
$x + 10y \geq 20$
$4 < y < 10$

_____

25. $7x + 2y > 14$
$2x - 7y > 14$
$3 < x < 4$

26. $4x + 2y > 0$
$2x + 5y \geq 20$
$4 \leq y < 6$

_____

27. $y - 2x < 3$
$2y > x + 4$
$3 < y < 4$

28. $2x - 3 \geq y$
$x + 2 < 2y$
$2y \leq x + 3$
$y < 5$

_____

29. $3y < -x + 6$
$x + 6 < 2y$
$-x - 4 < 3y$
$y < 3$

30. $2y \leq x - 8$
$y < -8$
$8 \leq 2y - 4x$
$x < -7$

_____

INTERMEDIATE ALGEBRA 2ND EDITION

Practice Problem Worksheets

CHAPTER 4: POLYNOMIALS

Chapter 4 Section 1: Adding and Subtracting Polynomials

Problems

For problems 1-10, find the degree of each polynomial.

1. $4x$

1

2. $3z^4$

4

3. $-13xz^3$

4

4. $15x^4y^3z^2$

9

5. 5

 0

6. $2 - 3x + 3x^5$

5

7. $2x^3y^5z^8 - 3x^2y^5z^9 - 45xz^3$

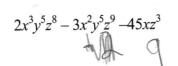 9

8. $13 + 7x^2y + xy^2z^3$

6

$13 + 3 + 6$
21 $3 \cdot 5$

9. $6x^{12} + x^2y^2z^{10}$

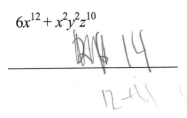 14

$12 + 11$ 11

10. $2x^2y^2z^3 - 3x^5y^4z^2$

11

$7 - 11$

For problems 11-24, perform the indicated operation.

11. $(6 - 7x + 8x^2) - (5 + 2x - 9x^2)$

$1 - 9x + 7x^2$

12. $(2 - 3u + 9u^2) + (4 + 3u - u^2)$

$6 + 8u^2$

13. $(3x^2 - 23x + 8) + (-4x^2 + 10x + 6)$

$7x^2 + 10x + 14$

14. $(8y^2 - 7y + 10) - (-9y^2 + 2y + 9)$

$17y^2 - 9y + 1$

15. $(10x^2 - 3x + 3) + (-4x^2 - 12x + 9)$

$6x^2 + 9x + 12$

16. $(2x^2 - 4x + 5) - (-3x^2 - 5x - 6)$

$5x^2 + x + 11$

17. $(12t^2 - 7t + 6) + (-2t^2 + 11t + 3)$

18. $(x^2 - 6x + 2) + (2x^2 - 7x + 4)$

19. $(7x^2 - 4x + 2) - (-x^2 - 3x - 7)$

20. $(5a^2 - 3a + 1) + (3a^2 - 9a - 1)$

21. $(5 - 3x^3y^3 + 3x^4y^5) - (4x^3y^3 - 3x^4y^5 - 2)$

22. $(4x^2y^6 - 6x^2y^4 + 1) - (4x^2y^6 - 8x^2y^4 - 2)$

23. $(2a^3b^5 + 3ab - 3a^3b) - (2a^3b^5 - 6ab - 4a^3b)$

24. $(9x^2y^6 - 7x^2y^4 + 3) - (5x^2y^6 - 6x^2y^4 - 1)$

For problems 25-28, write each polynomial in descending order.

25. $3x^2y^3z^2 - 5x^2y^6 + 2x^6z^4 - y^5z^6$

$-y^5z^6 + 2x^6z^4 - 5x^2y^6 + 3x^2y^3z^2$

26. $10xy^4z^2 - 3x^3y - 5x^6z^6 + y^3z^6$

$-5x^6z^6 + y^3z^6 + 10xy^4z^2 - 3x^3y$

27. $15u^4v^3 + 10u^2v^4 - 3u^5v^7 - 20uv$

28. $12w^2z^2 + 10w^2z^4 - 3w^5z^3 - 2w^5z^5$

For problems 29-33, evaluate the given function at the given value.

29. $F(x) = 3x^2 + 4x - 2$, $x = -3$

$-3 = 3x^2 + 4x - 2$

$3x^2 + 4x + 1$

$-3 = 27 - 12 - 2$

$-3 = 13$

16

30. $g(x) = 2x^2 - 6x - 5$, $x = -2$

$-2 = 2x^2 - 6x - 5$

$2x^2 - 6x - 3$

$4 \quad 15$

$8 + 12 - 5$

31. $f(x) = 3 + 4x - x^2$, $x = 5$

32. $G(x) = 6x^2 - 6x - 66$, $x = 6$

33. $Q(x) = 5 + 20x - x^2$, $x = -3$

Chapter 4 Section 1: Adding and Subtracting Polynomials

For problems 34-40, evaluate the given function at the given value.

34. $f(x) = 7x^2 - 8$, $f(3) = ?$

35. $g(u) = u^2 - 6u$, $g(2) = ?$

_____

_____

36. $h(x) = 9 + 2x - 2x^2$, $h(2) = ?$

37. $W(t) = 2t^2 - 3t - 5$, $W(3) = ?$

_____

_____

38. $f(x) = 3x^2 + 4x - 2$, $f(1) = ?$

39. $F(t) = 5 - 10x - 3x^2$, $F(-1) = ?$

_____

_____

40. $g(u) = 7u^2 - 2u - 1$, $g(2) = ?$

_____

Problems

For each problem, multiply the given expressions.

1. $\left(-3x^5\right)\left(4x^2\right)$

$-12x^7$

2. $\left(6y^3\right)\left(-8y^6\right)$

$-48y^9$

3. $\left(-12z^8\right)\left(-5z^9\right)$

$60z^{17}$

4. $\left(2y^7\right)\left(7y^5\right)$

$14y^{12}$

5. $\left(-5xy^4\right)\left(7x^4y^8\right)$

$-35x^5y^{12}$

6. $\left(-4a^8b\right)\left(-9ab^3\right)$

$36a^9b^4$

7. $\left(10u^2v^5w^2\right)\left(7u^5v^4w^3\right)$

$70u^7v^9w^5$

8. $\left(-2x^2y^3z^2\right)\left(9x^3y^4z^5\right)$

$-18x^5y^7z^7$

9. $\left(-5x^3y^2\right)\left(-2x^4y^2\right)\left(-3x^2y^6\right)$

$-30x^9y^{10}$

10. $\left(4u^3v\right)\left(-5u^2v^2\right)\left(6uv^3\right)$

$-120u^6v^6$

11. $2x^5\left(3x^3-4x\right)$

$(-x^2)(2x^5)=-2x^7$

12. $5a^4\left(2a^2+7a\right)$

$7a^3(5a^4)\quad 35a^7\quad 10a^6\ 17a^0$

13. $3u^6\left(3u^3-8u^2\right)$

$9u^9-24u^8$

$-5u(3v^6)\ -15u^5\quad -13u^0$

14. $-10x^5\left(3x^6-4x\right)$

$-x^5(-10x^5)\cdot+10x^{50}$

15. $\left(-3a^3b^4\right)\left(8a^5b^3-4ab^7+7b^3\right)\frac{4}{4}$

$(-3a^3b^4)\left(\frac{11a^4}{b^1}\right)\ -33a^7b^3$

16. $\left(-x^3y^4\right)\left(-2x^2y^4+4x^3y-2x^4y^3\right)$

$(-x^3y^4)(x^9y^8)$

$-x^{12}y^{12}$

17. $(u - 2v)(u - 4v)$

$u^2 - 4vu \, \overline{\rlap{/}=} \, 2vv \rlap{/}+ 8v^2$
$\qquad 2v^2 - 2vu + 8v^2$
$\qquad\qquad u^2 - 6vu + 8v^2$

18. $(2x - 4)(3x + 2)$

$6x^2 + 4x - 12x - 8 \qquad 6x^2 - 8x - 8$

19. $(4x - 3)(4x + 1)$

$16x^2 + 4x - 12x - 3$
$\qquad 16x^2 - 8x - 3$

20. $(5x - 4)(5x - 7)$

$25x^2 - 35x - 20x + 28$
$\qquad 25x^2 - 55x + 28$

21. $(6z + 1)(2z + 3)$

$12z^2 + 18z + 2z + 3$
$\qquad 12z^2 + 20z + 3$

22. $(4x - 7)(2x^2 + 3x - 1)$

$8x^3 + 12x - 4x - 14x^2 - 21x + 7$
$\qquad 8x^3$

23. $(5x - 2)(3x^2 - 4x - 2)$

24. $(2y + 5)(7y^2 - 6y + 5)$

25. $(6u - 1)(5u^2 - u - 2)$

26. $(6x - 7)(36x^2 + 42x + 49)$

27. $(x^2 - 2x + 1)(3x^2 + 2x - 1)$

28. $(2x^2 - x + 3)(3x^2 - 5x + 2)$

29. $(3y^2 - 4y + 5)(y^2 - 2y - 3)$

30. $(u^2 + 3u - 5)(u^2 - 3u + 5)$

31. $(2a^2 + a - 3)(2a^2 - a + 3)$

32. $(6v^2 - v - 4)(6v^2 + v + 4)$

33. $(x - 3)(x + 3)$

34. $(z + 5)(z - 5)$

35. $\left(3xy^2 - 8\right)\left(3xy^2 + 8\right)$

_____

36. $\left(5u^3v^4 - 2\right)\left(5u^3v^4 + 2\right)$

_____

37. $\left(6A^2 + 7B^3\right)\left(6A^2 - 7B^3\right)$

_____

38. $\left(9x^4 + 5\right)\left(9x^4 - 5\right)$

_____

39. $\left(4ab^2 + cd^2\right)\left(4ab^2 - cd^2\right)$

_____

40. $\left(5x^2y^4 - 2z^3\right)\left(5x^2y^4 + 2z^3\right)$

_____

Problems

Factor each polynomial, or write "prime" if the given polynomial cannot be factored.

1. $6x + 36$

$6(x + 6)6)$

2. $10x + 120$

$10(x + 12)$

3. $15x^2y^3 + 35x^2y^2$

$3x^2y^2(5y + 35)$

4. $99u^4v^3 + 44u^2v^3$

$11u^2v^3(9v^2 + 4)$

5. $25b^2 - 36a^2$

$(5b - 6a)^2$

6. $49z^2 - 9y^2$

$(9z - 3y)^2$

7. $100x^2 - 81$

prime $(10x - 9)^2$

8. $36A^2 - 1$

$(6a - 1)^2$

9. $25t^2 - 40t + 16$

$(5t - 4)^2$

10. $9x^2 + 66x + 121$

11. $36y^2 - 60y + 25$

$(6y - 5)^2$

12. $4x^4y^2 + 12x^2y + 9$

$(2x^2y + 3)^2$

13. $49a^6 - 4b^2$

$(7a^3 - 2b)^2$

14. $64x^4 - 169y^{10}$

$(8x^2 - 13y^5)^2$

15. $900z^8 - 1$

$(30z^4 - 1)^2$

16. $6AB - 9AD + 10BC - 15CD$

$(2B - 3D)(3A + 5C)$

17. $10x^2 - 2xy + 15xy - 3y^2$

$5x - xy + 5xy - 3y^2$
$2x(5x - y) 3y(5x - y)$

18. $6u^2 + 8uv - 9uv - 12v^2$

$2u(3v + 4v) - 3(3u - 4v)$

19. $10x^2 - 35x + 6x - 21$

$5x(2x - 7) + 3(2x - 7)$

20. $6x^2 + 2x + 27x + 9$

$2x(3x + 1) + 9(3x + 1)$

21. $16x^2 + 44x + 12x + 33$

$4x(4x + 11) + 3(4x + 11)$

22. $25x^2 - 10x + 15x - 6$

$5x(5x - 2) + 3(5x - 2)$

101

23. $14x^2 - 63x + 6x - 27$

$7x(2x-9) + 3(2x-9)$

$(7x+3)(2x-9)$

24. $y^2 - 16y + 63$

25. $z^2 - 2z - 48$

26. $x^2 + 17x + 60$

27. $x^2 - 19x + 78$

28. $t^2 - 8t - 105$

29. $4x^2 - 16x - 9$

30. $5x^2 + 38x + 21$

31. $3z^2 - 25z + 8$

32. $2y^2 + 11y - 63$

33. $8x^2 - 34x + 35$

34. $x^3 + 27$

35. $x^4 + 9$

36. $z^3 - 216$

37. $a^3 - 64$

38. $8x^3 + 125$

39. $27y^9 + 1$

40. $x^3 - 64$

41. $8u^3 - 27v^6$

42. $x^2 + x + 2$

43. $x^2 + 2x - 7$

44. $x^2 + 49$

Problems

Use long division to divide each expression.

1. $\dfrac{4x-2}{x-3}$

2. $\dfrac{5x+1}{x-6}$

3. $\dfrac{12x-8}{2x-1}$

4. $\dfrac{9x+6}{3x+4}$

5. $\dfrac{30x-15}{5x-2}$

6. $\dfrac{20x+4}{4x-2}$

7. $\dfrac{5x+30}{5x-2}$

8. $\dfrac{6x+1}{2x+3}$

9. $\dfrac{2x^2+4x+1}{x+1}$

10. $\dfrac{6x^2-3x+5}{x-4}$

11. $\dfrac{5x^2-7x-3}{x+4}$

12. $\dfrac{3x^2+2x+12}{x-6}$

13. $\dfrac{8x^2-7x+2}{x-2}$

14. $\dfrac{4x^2+2x+1}{x+8}$

15. $\dfrac{5x^3-3x^2+2x-1}{x-1}$

16. $\dfrac{2x^3-6x^2+3x-2}{x-4}$

(handwritten work in right margin and bottom)

$$x-6\ \overline{\smash{)}\ 5x+1} \quad 5$$
$$\underline{5x-30}$$
$$31$$

$$5+\frac{31}{x-6}$$

$$2x-1\ \overline{\smash{)}\ 12x-8} \quad 6$$
$$\underline{12x-6}$$
$$-2$$

$$6+\frac{-2}{2x-1}$$

$$3x+4\ \overline{\smash{)}\ 9x+6} \quad 3$$
$$\underline{-\ 9x+12}$$
$$-6$$

$$3+\frac{-6}{3x+4}$$

$$5x-2\ \overline{\smash{)}\ 30x-15} \quad 6$$
$$\underline{30x-12}$$
$$-3$$

$$6+\frac{-3}{5x-2}$$

$$4x-2\ \overline{\smash{)}\ 20x+4} \quad 5$$
$$\underline{20x-10}$$
$$14$$

$$5+\frac{14}{4x-2}$$

$$5x-2\ \overline{\smash{)}\ 5x+30} \quad 1$$
$$\underline{5x-2}$$
$$32$$

$$1+\frac{32}{5x-2}$$

17. $\dfrac{x^4 + 4x^3 + 6x^2 + 4x + 1}{x^3 + 3x^2 + 3x + 1}$

$x^4 + 4x^3 + 3x^2 + x\,1$

18. $\dfrac{2x^4 - 3x^3 + 4x^2 - 5x + 6}{x^3 + x^2 + x + 1}$

$\dfrac{2x^4}{x^4}$

19. $\dfrac{5x^4 - 4x^3 + 3x^2 - 2x + 1}{x^3 + x^2 - x - 2}$

20. $\dfrac{3x^4 + x^3 - 8x^2 + x + 3}{x^3 - 2x^2 + 2x - 1}$

21. $\dfrac{x^4 + 2x^3 + 3x^2 + 4x + 5}{x^3 + 2x^2 + 3x + 4}$

22. $\dfrac{2x^4 - 4x^3 + 3x^2 - 4x + 5}{x^3 + 2x^2 + 2x + 1}$

23. $\dfrac{x^4 - 4x^3 - 6x^2 + 3x - 2}{x^3 - x^2 + 2x - 1}$

24. $\dfrac{x^4 + 5x^3 - 2x^2 + 4x + 3}{x^3 - 2x^2 + x - 2}$

25. $\dfrac{x^3 + 5x^2 + 2}{x - 3}$

26. $\dfrac{x^3 + 7}{x - 1}$

27. $\dfrac{x^3 + 4x + 5}{x + 2}$

28. $\dfrac{x^3 - 8}{x - 1}$

29. $\dfrac{x^3 + 3}{x + 3}$

30. $\dfrac{5x^3 - 2x^2 + 1}{x - 2}$

31. $\dfrac{7x^3 + 6}{x - 1}$

32. $\dfrac{3x^3 + 33}{3x + 3}$

33. $\dfrac{x^3 + 8x^2}{x - 2}$

34. $\dfrac{x^4 + 8x^3 - 6x^2 - 9x + 2}{x^2 - 2x + 2}$

_____

_____

35. $\dfrac{x^4 + 2x^3 - 3x^2 + 5x - 4}{x^2 + x + 1}$

36. $\dfrac{x^4 + 2x - 3}{x^3 + x^2 + 1}$

_____

_____

37. $\dfrac{x^4 + 1}{x^3 + x^2 + x + 1}$

38. $\dfrac{x^4 - 16}{x^3 - x + 1}$

_____

_____

39. $\dfrac{x^4 - 4x^3 + 6x^2 - 4x + 1}{x^3 + 3x^2 + 3x + 1}$

40. $\dfrac{x^5 + 1}{x^3 + 1}$

_____

_____

Problems

For problems 1-33, find the solution set of each equation.

1. $(x - 6)(x + 3) = 0$

2. $(2x - 5)(5x - 2) = 0$

_____

_____

3. $x(2x + 1) = 0$

4. $(7x + 2)(6x + 11) = 0$

_____

_____

5. $(x + 22)(x - 13) = 0$

6. $(6x - 5)(2x + 9) = 0$

_____

_____

7. $(x + 1)(x - 1)(x - 3) = 0$

8. $(x - 8)(4x - 1)(x + 7) = 0$

_____

_____

9. $x^2 + 6x - 55 = 0$

10. $x^2 + 2x - 63 = 0$

_____

_____

11. $x^2 = 2x + 48$

12. $x^2 = 12x - 11$

_____

_____

13. $3x^2 - 35 = x(x + 9)$

14. $2(3x^2 - 2) = 5x$

_____

_____

15. $x(17 - x) = 66$

16. $2x^2 = 9x + 5$

_____

_____

17. $2x(3x^2 + 7) = 25x^2$

_____

18. $2x^2(3 - 4x) = x$

_____

19. $x^2(x - 4) = 3x^2(x - 3) - 12x$

_____

20. $2x^2(3x - 7) = 3x^2(x - 3) + 2x$

_____

21. $3x(x - 5) = x(x + 4) - 24$

_____

22. $5x(x - 4) = 2x(x - 9) + 5$

_____

23. $(x - 1)^2 - 10(x - 1) + 24 = 0$

_____

24. $(z - 2)^2 + 4(z - 2) - 77 = 0$

_____

25. $(y + 3)^2 - 13(y + 3) + 42 = 0$

_____

26. $\left(x^2 - 7x + 14\right)^2 - 6\left(x^2 - 7x + 14\right) + 8 = 0$

_____

27. $\left(x^2 - 8x + 3\right)^2 + 13\left(x^2 - 8x + 3\right) + 36 = 0$

28. $\left(x^2 - 10x + 5\right)^2 + 15\left(x^2 - 10x + 5\right) + 44 = 0$

_____

29. $\left(x^2 + x + 2\right)^2 - \left(x^2 - 8\right)^2 = 0$

_____

30. $\left(x^2 + x - 6\right)^2 - \left(x^2 + 3\right)^2 = 0$

_____

31. $\left(x^2 - 2x - 20\right)^2 - \left(x^2 - 4\right)^2 = 0$

_____

32. $\left(x^2 - 4x - 1\right)^2 - \left(x^2 - 5\right)^2 = 0$

_____

33. $\left(x^2 + 3x - 3\right)^2 - \left(x^2 + 4\right)^2 = 0$

_____

34.   Solve for x in the depicted right triangle:

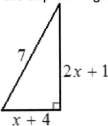

_____

35.   Solve for x in the depicted right triangle:

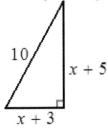

_____

36.   Solve for x in the depicted right triangle:

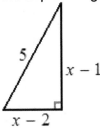

_____

37.   Solve for x in the depicted right triangle:

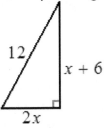

_____

38.   Consider three consecutive positive integers, such that the sum of the squares of the two larger integers is 5 more than 28 times the smaller one. Find the smaller integer.

_____

39.   Consider three consecutive positive integers, such that the sum of the squares of the two larger integers is 4 less than 25 times the smaller one. Find the smaller integer.

_____

40.   Consider three consecutive positive odd integers, such that the sum of the squares of the two larger integers is 20 more than 54 times the smaller one. Find the smaller integer.

_____

INTERMEDIATE ALGEBRA 2ND EDITION

Practice Problem Worksheets

CHAPTER 5: RATIONAL EXPRESSIONS

Problems

Simplify each rational expression in problems 1-24 by reducing the expression to lowest terms.

1. $\dfrac{20}{35}$

2. $\dfrac{78}{66}$

3. $\dfrac{360}{504}$

4. $\dfrac{216}{324}$

5. $\dfrac{60x}{80x}$

6. $\dfrac{24y^2}{112y}$

7. $\dfrac{a^3b^4c^2}{ab^2c^4}$

8. $\dfrac{20x^4y^2z}{15xy^2z^4}$

9. $\dfrac{7uv}{7u-21}$

10. $\dfrac{6x^2y}{3x^2y+30xy}$

11. $\dfrac{x^3-1}{x^3-2x^2+x}$

12. $\dfrac{2x^2-6x+18}{2x^4+54x}$

13. $\dfrac{9-z}{z^2-81}$

14. $\dfrac{49-t^2}{t+7}$

15. $\dfrac{a^2-4b^2}{4b^2-4ab+a^2}$

16. $\dfrac{25x^2-9y^2}{25x^2+30xy+9y^2}$

17. $\dfrac{x^2 - 2x - 63}{x^2 - x - 72}$

18. $\dfrac{x^2 - 14x + 33}{x^2 - 5x - 66}$

19. $\dfrac{66x^2 - 77xy + 60xy - 70y^2}{11x + 10y}$

20. $\dfrac{6x^3 - 10x^2y + 9xy^2 - 15y^3}{3x - 5y}$

21. $\dfrac{x^2 - 2xy + 4y^2}{x^3 + 8y^3}$

22. $\dfrac{25A^2 + 15AB + 9B^2}{125A^3 - 27B^3}$

23. $\dfrac{9r^2 - 16s^2}{3r^2 - 2rs - 8s^2}$

24. $\dfrac{25x^2 - 4y^2}{25x^2 - 20xy + 4y^2}$

Perform the indicated operations in 25-40, and reduce to lowest terms.

25. $\dfrac{130x}{49y} \cdot \dfrac{7y}{10x^2}$

26. $\dfrac{8R}{21r} \cdot \dfrac{105r}{24R}$

27. $\dfrac{x^2 - 2x - 48}{x^2 - 2x - 24} \cdot \dfrac{x - 6}{x - 8}$

28. $\dfrac{x^2 - 16x + 55}{x^2 + 12x + 27} \cdot \dfrac{x + 9}{x - 11}$

29. $\dfrac{t^2}{3t + 18} \cdot \dfrac{t^2 - 36}{t^2 - 6t}$

30. $\dfrac{-z}{2z + 9} \cdot \dfrac{81 - 4z^2}{2z^2 - 9z}$

31. $\dfrac{2x^2 - 14x + 24}{x^2 + 12x + 27} \cdot \dfrac{x^2 + 9x}{2x - 8}$

32. $\dfrac{5x^2 - 20x - 160}{x^2 - 8x + 12} \cdot \dfrac{x^2 - 6x}{5x^2 - 40x}$

33. $\dfrac{12x - 3xy^2}{4x^2 - 36x + 32} \cdot \dfrac{2x^2 - 16x}{6x - 3xy}$

34. $\dfrac{4a^3 - 4a^2 - 8a}{a^2b - 7ab + 12b} \cdot \dfrac{a^2b - 4ab}{4a^3 - 8a^2}$

35. $\dfrac{14x}{15y} \div \dfrac{7x^2}{5y^2}$

36. $\dfrac{42u^2}{35v^2} \div \dfrac{6u^2v}{7uv^2}$

37. $\dfrac{x^2 - 17x + 72}{x^2 - 11x + 28} \div \dfrac{x^2 - 12x + 32}{x^2 - 16x + 63}$

38. $\dfrac{x^2 - 8x - 20}{x^2 - 64} \div \dfrac{x^2 - 20x + 100}{x^2 - 6x - 16}$

39. $\dfrac{9x^2 - 25}{y^2 - x^2} \cdot \dfrac{xy^2 - x^3}{6x^2 - 7x - 5} \div \dfrac{3x + 5}{2x^2 + x}$

40. $\dfrac{4u^2 - 49}{4v^2 - u^2} \cdot \dfrac{4v^3 - u^2v}{2u^2 - 3u - 35} \div \dfrac{2u - 7}{v}$

Problems

Add/subtract and simplify the expressions in each problem.

1. $\dfrac{2x^2 + 2x - 15}{x - 4} - \dfrac{x^2 + 9}{x - 4}$

2. $\dfrac{y(y + 6)}{y + 12} + \dfrac{y - 60}{y + 12}$

3. $\dfrac{3x^2 - 4x + 22}{x + 8} - \dfrac{2x^2 - 6x + 70}{x + 8}$

4. $\dfrac{2t(t - 15)}{t - 10} + \dfrac{50 + 15t - t^2}{t - 10}$

5. $\dfrac{3x^2 - 26}{x - 7} - \dfrac{2x^2 + 4x - 5}{x - 7}$

6. $\dfrac{2x(x - 4)}{x - 9} - \dfrac{x^2 + 9}{x - 9}$

7. $\dfrac{5z^2 - 8}{2z + 1} + \dfrac{11 + 7z - 3z^2}{2z + 1}$

8. $\dfrac{5 - x - x^2}{x + 6} - \dfrac{65 + 3x - 2x^2}{x + 6}$

9. $\dfrac{2x}{yz} - \dfrac{3y}{xz} - \dfrac{5z}{xy}$

10. $\dfrac{2}{A} + \dfrac{7}{AB} + \dfrac{3}{B}$

11. $\dfrac{u}{vw} - \dfrac{w}{uv} + \dfrac{v}{uw}$

12. $\dfrac{4}{x} + \dfrac{3}{x - 2}$

13. $\dfrac{5}{x} - \dfrac{1}{x - 5}$

14. $\dfrac{2}{z + 3} - \dfrac{3}{z - 6}$

15. $\dfrac{10}{y - 5} + \dfrac{5}{y - 10}$

16. $\dfrac{4}{3x} + \dfrac{2}{15x} - \dfrac{3}{5x^2}$

17. $\dfrac{5}{2u} - \dfrac{4}{7u} + \dfrac{3}{14u^2}$

18. $\dfrac{2}{45} - \dfrac{5}{9y} - \dfrac{9}{5y^2}$

19. $\dfrac{x}{6} + \dfrac{1}{4x} - \dfrac{4}{3x^2}$

20. $\dfrac{1}{z+12} + \dfrac{z+26}{z^2+10z-24}$

21. $\dfrac{x-2}{x-8} - \dfrac{9x+6}{x^2-3x-40}$

22. $\dfrac{t}{5-t} + \dfrac{2t^2+3t-54}{t^2+t-30}$

23. $\dfrac{2w}{w+1} - \dfrac{w^2+22w+40}{w^2+21w+20}$

24. $\dfrac{x}{x+1} - \dfrac{1}{x-2} + \dfrac{3}{x+1} + \dfrac{6}{(x+1)(x-2)}$

25. $\dfrac{3x}{x+3} - \dfrac{2}{x-5} - \dfrac{2x^2-22x+44}{(x+3)(x-5)}$

26. $\dfrac{5y}{y-9} + \dfrac{4}{y-8} - \dfrac{4y^2-31y}{(y-9)(y-8)}$

27. $\dfrac{1}{a-b} - \dfrac{a}{a^2-b^2} - \dfrac{b}{a^2+2ab+b^2}$

28. $\dfrac{x+3}{x+5} - \dfrac{x-5}{x-4} + \dfrac{2x-17}{x^2+x-20}$

29. $\dfrac{2y-3}{y+8} - \dfrac{y^2-2y-118}{y^2+18y+80}$

30. $\dfrac{2}{M^2-36} - \dfrac{3}{6-M}$

31. $\dfrac{5}{25-u^2}+\dfrac{1}{u-5}$

32. $\dfrac{6x-9}{4x^2-81}-\dfrac{2}{2x+9}$

33. $\dfrac{15w+5}{9w^2-1}+\dfrac{6}{1-3w}$

34. $\dfrac{x-2}{x^2-2x+4}+\dfrac{4-x-x^2}{x^3+8}$

35. $\dfrac{x-1}{x^2+3x+9}+\dfrac{1+x-x^2}{x^3-27}$

36. $\dfrac{2t-3}{4t^2-10t+25}+\dfrac{1-4t-2t^2}{8t^3+125}$

37. $\dfrac{x-3}{9x^2+12x+16}+\dfrac{1+5x-3x^2}{27x^3-64}$

38. $\dfrac{y^3-8}{y^2+3y-10}-\dfrac{y^3+8}{y^2+7y+10}$

39. $\dfrac{x^3-64}{x^2+3x-28}-\dfrac{x^3+64}{x^2+11x+28}-\dfrac{7x}{x+7}$

40. $\dfrac{125-8x^3}{-2x^2+3x+5}-\dfrac{125+8x^3}{2x^2+7x+5}-\dfrac{19x}{x+1}$

Problems

Simplify each complex rational expression.

1. $\dfrac{\dfrac{1}{2}+\dfrac{1}{6}}{\dfrac{5}{6}-\dfrac{2}{3}}$

2. $\dfrac{\dfrac{3}{5}-\dfrac{7}{10}}{\dfrac{1}{10}-\dfrac{3}{2}}$

3. $\dfrac{\dfrac{2}{21}+\dfrac{7}{3}}{\dfrac{5}{7}+\dfrac{4}{21}}$

4. $\dfrac{\dfrac{23}{24}-\dfrac{5}{12}}{\dfrac{5}{6}+\dfrac{7}{24}}$

5. $\dfrac{\dfrac{2}{B}+\dfrac{3}{AB}}{\dfrac{3}{AB}-\dfrac{2}{B}}$

6. $\dfrac{\dfrac{1}{x}-\dfrac{3}{xy}}{\dfrac{2}{y}-\dfrac{1}{x}}$

7. $\dfrac{\dfrac{4}{u^2v}-\dfrac{1}{uv}}{\dfrac{1}{u^2}+\dfrac{3}{uv}}$

8. $\dfrac{\dfrac{7}{x^2}+\dfrac{1}{y^2}}{\dfrac{1}{xy}+\dfrac{4}{x^2y^2}}$

9. $\dfrac{\dfrac{6}{a^2}-\dfrac{2}{b}}{\dfrac{8}{a}-\dfrac{6}{b^2}}$

10. $\dfrac{\dfrac{5}{2xy}-\dfrac{2}{y}}{\dfrac{3}{2x}+\dfrac{1}{2y}}$

11.
$$\dfrac{\dfrac{8x}{7}}{\dfrac{20x}{21}}$$

12.
$$\dfrac{\dfrac{A+1}{25B^2}}{\dfrac{(A+1)^2}{5B}}$$

13.
$$\dfrac{\dfrac{2a}{9b}}{\dfrac{6a}{15b}}$$

14.
$$\dfrac{\dfrac{30xz}{35y^2}}{\dfrac{18x^2}{49yz}}$$

15.
$$\dfrac{\dfrac{2}{x+2}}{\dfrac{2x}{x+2}}$$

16.
$$\dfrac{\dfrac{2A-B}{AB+1}}{\dfrac{B-2A}{2AB+2}}$$

17.
$$\dfrac{\dfrac{x-5}{x^2+6x+9}}{\dfrac{x^2-10x+25}{x+3}}$$

18.
$$\dfrac{\dfrac{x^2-5x-24}{x^2+x-20}}{\dfrac{x^2-9x+8}{x^2-2x-8}}$$

19.
$$\dfrac{2-\dfrac{1}{Y}}{1+\dfrac{3}{Y}}$$

20.
$$\dfrac{2A-\dfrac{1}{AB}}{B+\dfrac{2A}{B}}$$

21.
$$\dfrac{5-\dfrac{3}{2z}}{5+\dfrac{2}{3z}}$$

22.
$$\dfrac{\dfrac{3}{4x}-7}{2+\dfrac{5}{4x}}$$

23.
$$\dfrac{\dfrac{5}{3u^2} - \dfrac{2}{9u}}{\dfrac{7}{9u^2} - \dfrac{2}{3u}}$$

24.
$$\dfrac{\dfrac{8}{5x^2} + \dfrac{7}{20x}}{\dfrac{7}{20x^2} - \dfrac{3}{5x}}$$

25.
$$\dfrac{\dfrac{4}{w+1} + \dfrac{2}{w}}{\dfrac{2w}{w+1} - \dfrac{2}{w}}$$

26.
$$\dfrac{\dfrac{3}{z-2} - \dfrac{1}{2z}}{\dfrac{5}{2z} - \dfrac{2}{z-2}}$$

27.
$$\dfrac{\dfrac{4}{2(x+4)} - \dfrac{2}{3x}}{\dfrac{5}{6x} + \dfrac{1}{3(x+4)}}$$

28.
$$\dfrac{\dfrac{9}{t-3} + \dfrac{3}{7t}}{\dfrac{6}{7(t-3)} + \dfrac{5}{t-3}}$$

29.
$$\dfrac{x}{x - \dfrac{x}{x-1}}$$

30.
$$\dfrac{2A}{3A + \dfrac{2A}{3A+1}}$$

31.
$$\dfrac{y}{2y + \dfrac{3y}{4y+1}}$$

32.
$$\dfrac{2x}{5x - \dfrac{2x}{5x-2}}$$

33.
$$\dfrac{\dfrac{5}{x-3} - \dfrac{3}{x^2+3x-18}}{\dfrac{3}{x^2+3x-18} + \dfrac{2}{x+6}}$$

34.
$$\dfrac{\dfrac{7}{x+5} - \dfrac{2}{x^2-6x-55}}{\dfrac{5}{x^2-6x-55} - \dfrac{3}{x-11}}$$

35.
$$\dfrac{\dfrac{3}{x-1}+\dfrac{2x}{x^2+3x-4}}{\dfrac{2x}{x^2+3x-4}+\dfrac{3}{x+4}}$$

36.
$$\dfrac{\dfrac{4}{2x-1}+\dfrac{3x}{2x^2-11x+5}}{\dfrac{4x}{2x^2-11x+5}-\dfrac{3}{x-5}}$$

37.
$$\dfrac{\dfrac{5}{r^2-9}-\dfrac{2}{r-3}}{\dfrac{r}{r+3}-\dfrac{4}{r-3}+\dfrac{1}{r^2-9}}$$

38.
$$\dfrac{\dfrac{2}{y^2-25}-\dfrac{2}{y+5}}{\dfrac{y}{y+5}+\dfrac{3}{y-5}-\dfrac{39}{y^2-25}}$$

39.
$$\dfrac{\dfrac{x}{x+1}+\dfrac{13}{x-1}-\dfrac{58}{x^2-1}}{\dfrac{x}{x-1}+\dfrac{16}{x+1}+\dfrac{46}{x^2-1}}$$

40.
$$\dfrac{\dfrac{z}{z+4}+\dfrac{4}{z-4}+\dfrac{5}{z^2-16}}{\dfrac{z}{z+4}-\dfrac{4}{z-4}+\dfrac{5}{z^2-16}}$$

Problems

Solve each equation.

1. $\dfrac{3}{2x} + \dfrac{2}{3x} = 1$

2. $\dfrac{1}{3t} - \dfrac{3}{t} = 2$

_____

3. $\dfrac{1}{x} + \dfrac{x}{x-1} = 1$

4. $\dfrac{5}{x} + \dfrac{2x}{x-3} = 2$

_____

5. $\dfrac{3x}{x+5} - \dfrac{4}{x} = 3$

6. $\dfrac{4}{Q+3} - \dfrac{6}{Q+4} = \dfrac{Q}{Q^2 + 7Q + 12}$

_____

7. $\dfrac{1}{x+7} = \dfrac{x-7}{x^2 + 6x - 7} + \dfrac{7}{x-1}$

8. $\dfrac{6}{x-4} + \dfrac{7}{x-8} = \dfrac{x+3}{x^2 - 12x + 32}$

_____

9. $\dfrac{2}{x-5} = \dfrac{2x+5}{x^2 + 4x - 45} + \dfrac{9}{x+9}$

10. $\dfrac{11}{y+4} - \dfrac{4}{y-6} = \dfrac{3y+1}{y^2 - 2y - 24}$

_____

11. $\dfrac{9}{x+2} = \dfrac{7}{x}$

12. $\dfrac{3}{s} = \dfrac{8}{s-6}$

_____

13. $\dfrac{3}{x-3} = \dfrac{13}{x}$

14. $\dfrac{1}{x} = \dfrac{3}{x-1}$

_____

15. $\dfrac{t+2}{t+4} = \dfrac{t-4}{t+2}$

16. $\dfrac{x+7}{x+2} = \dfrac{5}{x+2}$

17. $\dfrac{R-7}{R+1} = \dfrac{R-6}{R+2}$

18. $\dfrac{2x+5}{x-2} = \dfrac{6x-3}{3x+1}$

19. $\dfrac{6u+1}{4u-2} = \dfrac{3u-3}{2u+4}$

20. $\dfrac{3x+2}{5x-2} = \dfrac{x-3}{2x+3}$

21. $\dfrac{2x+2}{3x-2} = \dfrac{x-3}{2x+3}$

22. $\dfrac{3x-6}{4x-1} = \dfrac{x-2}{x+3}$

23. $\dfrac{5y-6}{3y-2} = \dfrac{y+6}{y+2}$

24. $3 - \dfrac{4}{x} = \dfrac{x}{x+3}$

25. $\dfrac{1}{2} - \dfrac{7}{x} = \dfrac{x}{2x+1}$

26. $-\dfrac{3}{4} + \dfrac{5}{V} = \dfrac{V}{2V-3}$

27. $-5 + \dfrac{3}{x} = \dfrac{3x}{x-10}$

28. $\dfrac{5}{x} - 1 = \dfrac{4x}{2x-1}$

29. $\dfrac{14}{t} + 8 = \dfrac{-t}{t+16}$

30. $\dfrac{1}{z-3} - \dfrac{3}{z^3-27} = \dfrac{z+1}{z^2+3z+9}$

31. $\dfrac{2}{W+2} - \dfrac{5}{W^3+8} = \dfrac{2W+1}{W^2-2W+4}$

32. $\dfrac{3}{y+4} - \dfrac{y+2}{y^2-4y+16} = \dfrac{3y}{y^3+64}$

33. $\dfrac{2}{x+5} - \dfrac{x-5}{x^2-5x+25} = \dfrac{2x^2}{x^3+125}$

34. $\dfrac{3}{x-4} - \dfrac{x}{x^2+4x+16} = \dfrac{6x^2}{x^3-64}$

35. $\dfrac{1}{2t-3} - \dfrac{2t^2}{8t^3-27} = \dfrac{t-1}{4t^2+6t+9}$

36. $\dfrac{3}{y^2-4} - \dfrac{5}{y^3+8} = \dfrac{2}{y^2-2y+4}$

37. $\dfrac{2}{A^2-9} + \dfrac{9}{A^3-27} = \dfrac{1}{A^2+3A+9}$

38. $\dfrac{1}{x^2-25} - \dfrac{3}{x^3-125} = \dfrac{1}{x^2+5x+25}$

39. $\dfrac{2}{4u^2-1} + \dfrac{3}{8u^3-1} = \dfrac{1}{4u^2+2u+1}$

40. $\dfrac{3}{9x^2-1} + \dfrac{7}{27x^3+1} = \dfrac{4}{9x^2-3x+1}$

41. $1 - \dfrac{2x+3}{x^2+2x-3} = \dfrac{-x}{x^2+2x-3}$

42. $1 + \dfrac{33-2x}{x^2+8x-33} = \dfrac{55}{x^2+8x-33}$

Problems

Solve for the indicated variable in problems 1-26.

1. Solve for x: $y = mx + b$

2. Solve for x: $y = \dfrac{a}{mx}$

3. Solve for A: $2 = \dfrac{B}{A - C}$

4. Solve for y: $x = \dfrac{4}{5 - y}$

5. Solve for w: $u = \dfrac{w}{u + w}$

6. Solve for A: $B = \dfrac{C}{A - C}$

7. Solve for t_0: $v = \dfrac{x_1 + x_0}{t_1 + t_0}$

8. Solve for n: $m = \dfrac{2 + m}{m - n}$

9. Solve for A: $5 = \dfrac{2A + 3B}{2A}$

10. Solve for Y: $1 = \dfrac{3Y - W}{2Y}$

11. Solve for Q: $c - 2 = \dfrac{Q + 2c}{Q - c}$

12. Solve for y: $3 - x = \dfrac{x - 5y}{y}$

13. Solve for R_2: $\dfrac{1}{R_1} + \dfrac{1}{R_2} = \dfrac{1}{R}$

14. Solve for W: $\dfrac{U}{W} - \dfrac{1}{4} = \dfrac{V}{4W}$

15. Solve for y: $\dfrac{A}{y-2} - \dfrac{B}{y+2} = \dfrac{C}{y^2-4}$

16. Solve for A: $\dfrac{A}{B-1} + \dfrac{1}{A} = \dfrac{A-B}{B-1}$

---

17. Solve for s: $\dfrac{t}{t-s} - \dfrac{t}{t^2-s^2} = \dfrac{1}{t+s}$

18. Solve for B: $\dfrac{A}{A-2B} = \dfrac{A-1}{A+B} - \dfrac{3}{A-2B}$

---

19. Solve for x: $\dfrac{x}{x-2y} = \dfrac{x-1}{x+y} - \dfrac{3}{x-2y}$

20. Solve for Q: $\dfrac{4}{3t} = \dfrac{3t}{Q} - \dfrac{1}{Qt}$

---

21. Solve for v: $\dfrac{2}{5u} = \dfrac{2u}{v-1} + \dfrac{1}{3u}$

22. Solve for y: $\dfrac{2}{y} = \dfrac{x}{y+2} - \dfrac{2x}{y^2+2y}$

---

23. Solve for Q: $\dfrac{Q}{Q+t} = \dfrac{t}{t-3} + \dfrac{t}{Q+t}$

24. Solve for h: $\dfrac{2G}{2R-h} = \dfrac{V}{3R}$

---

25. Solve for A: $\dfrac{4B}{3B-2A} = \dfrac{1}{A}$

26. Solve for W: $\dfrac{e}{W-e} = \dfrac{e-1}{1-W}$

---

27. Suppose it takes 9 hours for machine A to shred a ton of documents, while it only takes 7 hours for machine B to accomplish the task. How long will it take to do the job with both machines working together? (Round off your answer to the nearest minute.)

---

28. If it takes 20 hours for Joe to paint a house and it takes 16 hours for Tom to paint the house, how long will it take them working together? (Round off your answer to the nearest minute.)

---

29.   Suppose it takes 4 hours for Mara to do her yard work. Working together with her son Ananda, it takes 3 hours to do the yard work. How long would it take for Ananda to do the yard work, working alone? (Round off your answer to the nearest minute.)

_____

30.   Suppose it takes 25 hours for robot A to construct a new robot. Working together with robot B, it takes 14 hours for both robots to construct a new robot. How long would it take robot B to construct a new robot, working alone? (Round off your answer to the nearest minute.)

_____

31.   Suppose it takes 15 hours for a pipe to fill a tank of water if the tank does not leak. However, our tank has a crack that will cause a full tank to leak out in 21 hours. If the tank starts off half full (or if you prefer, half empty!), how long will it take to completely fill the leaky tank?

_____

32.   Suppose it takes 3 hours for a pipe to fill a tank of water, if the tank does not leak. However, our tank has a crack that will cause a full tank to leak out in 5 hours. If the tank starts off two-thirds full, how long will it take to completely fill the leaky tank?

_____

33.   Suppose it takes 7 hours for a pipe to fill a tank of water, if the tank does not leak. However, our tank has a crack that will cause a full tank to leak out in 10 hours. If the tank starts off four-fifths full, how long will it take to completely fill the leaky tank?

_____

34.   Suppose it takes 13 hours for a pipe to fill a tank of water, if the tank does not leak. However, our tank has a crack that will cause a full tank to leak out in 17 hours. If the tank starts off empty, how long will it take to completely fill the leaky tank?

_____

35.   Suppose a bicycle traveling at a constant speed goes 65 miles. If the bicycle had gone three miles per hour faster, it could have gone 80 miles in the same amount of time. What was the bicycle's speed (in miles per hour)?

_____

36.   Suppose a car traveling at a constant speed goes 300 miles. If the car had gone eleven miles per hour faster, it could have gone 355 miles in the same amount of time. What was the car's speed (in miles per hour)?

_____

37. Suppose a train traveling at a constant speed goes 120 miles. If the train had gone eleven miles per hour faster, it could have gone 200 miles in the same amount of time. What was the train's speed (in miles per hour)?

_____

38. Suppose a plane travels a distance of 990 miles going with the wind, but would have only gone 750 miles flying against the wind for the same amount of time. If the speed of the plane in still air is 290 miles per hour, what is the speed of the wind (in miles per hour)?

_____

39. Suppose an airliner travels a distance of 3,135 miles going with the wind, but would have only gone 1,865 miles flying against the wind for the same amount of time. If the speed of the plane in still air is 500 miles per hour, what is the speed of the wind (in miles per hour)?

_____

40. Suppose a jet travels a distance of 3,880 miles going with the wind, but would have only gone 2,120 miles flying against the wind for the same amount of time. If the speed of the wind is 220 miles per hour, what would have been the speed of the jet in still air (in miles per hour)?

_____

Problems

For problems 1-7, give the exact solution.

1. Suppose that y is directly proportional to x, and $y = 12$ when $x = 5$. What is y, when $x = 7$?

2. Suppose that y is directly proportional to x, and $y = 3$ when $x = 8$. What is y, when $x = 6$?

3. Suppose that z is directly proportional to t, and $z = 22$ when $t = 15$. What is z, when $t = 2$?

4. Suppose that y is directly proportional to x, and $y = 5$ when $x = 8$. What is y, when $x = 53$?

5. Suppose that y is directly proportional to x, and $y = 75$ when $x = 45$. What is y, when $x = 22$?

6. Suppose that W is directly proportional to u, and $W = 32$ when $u = 31$. What is W when $u = 44$?

7. Suppose that y is directly proportional to x, and $y = 14$ when $x = 23$. What is y, when $x = 32$?

For problems 8-14, round your answer to the nearest tenth.

8. Suppose that W is directly proportional to m, and $W = 4.5$ when $m = 34.1$. What is W, when $m = 131.3$?

9. Suppose that y is directly proportional to x, and $y = 32.1$ when $x = 22.4$. What is y, when $x = 14.2$?

10. Suppose that Q is directly proportional to m, and $Q = 2.8$ when $m = 8.6$. What is Q, when $m = 21.3$?

11. Suppose that W is directly proportional to t, and $W = 67.5$ when $t = 22.1$. What is W, when $t = 11.5$?

12. Suppose that M is directly proportional to w, and $M = 6.3$ when $w = 23.1$. What is M, when $w = 12.5$?

13. Suppose that P is directly proportional to z, and $P = 21.5$ when $z = 14.3$. What is P, when $z = 23.5$?

14. Suppose that y is directly proportional to x, and $y = 18.5$ when $x = 6.9$. What is y, when $x = 30.2$?

For problems 15-34, give the exact solution.

15. Suppose that y is inversely proportional to x, and $y = 4$ when $x = 11$.
What is y, when $x = 7$?

16. Suppose that z is inversely proportional to t, and $z = 22$ when $t = 3$.
What is z, when $t = 11$?

---

17. Suppose that y is inversely proportional to x, and $y = 12$ when $x = 8$.
What is y, when $x = 34$?

18. Suppose that y is inversely proportional to x, and $y = 14$ when $x = 32$.
What is y, when $x = 23$?

---

19. Suppose that R is inversely proportional to t, and $R = 27$ when $t = 14$.
What is R, when $t = 17$?

20. Suppose that y is inversely proportional to x, and $y = 34$ when $x = 21$.
What is y, when $x = 3$?

---

21. Suppose that y is inversely proportional to x, and $y = 15$ when $x = 47$.
What is y, when $x = 27$?

22. Suppose that Z is inversely proportional to q, and $Z = 76$ when $q = 34$.
What is Z, when $q = 20$?

---

23. Suppose that r is inversely proportional to v, and $r = 42$ when $v = 32$.
What is v, if $r = 22$?

24. Suppose that A is inversely proportional to B, and $A = 23$ when $B = 11$.
What is B, if $A = 53$?

---

25. Suppose that y is inversely proportional to x, and $y = 12$ when $x = 14$.
What is x, if $y = 3$?

26. Suppose that A is inversely proportional to B, and $A = 83$ when $B = 76$.
What is B, if $A = 34$?

---

27. Suppose that y is inversely proportional to x, and $y = 55$ when $x = 64$.
What is x, if $y = 13$?

28. Suppose that z is inversely proportional to t, and $z = 15$ when $t = 22$.
What is t, if $z = 12$?

---

29. Suppose that A is inversely proportional to B, and $A = 37$ when $B = 23$.
What is B, if $A = 15$?

30. Suppose that z is jointly proportional to x and y, and $z = 41$ when $x = 4$ and $y = 13$.
What is z, when $x = 1$ and $y = 11$?

---

31. Suppose that Q is jointly proportional to u and v, and $Q = 21$ when $u = 13$ and $v = 20$. What is Q, when $u = 14$ and $v = 5$?

32. Suppose that z is jointly proportional to x and y, and $z = 26$ when $x = 2$ and $y = 6$. What is z, when $x = 3$ and $y = 5$?

_____

_____

33. Suppose that P is jointly proportional to n and m, and $P = 21$ when $n = 3$ and $m = 13$. What is P, when $n = 2$ and $m = 15$?

34. Suppose that z is jointly proportional to x and y, and $z = 17$ when $x = 27$ and $y = 12$. What is z, when $x=11$ and $y=10$?

_____

_____

For problems 35-41, round your answer to the nearest tenth.

35. Suppose that Q varies jointly with T and the square of W, and inversely with the cube of m. If $Q = 11$ when $T = 4$, $W = 7$, and $m = 4$, then find Q when $T = 1$, $W = 3$, and $m = 2$.

_____

36. Suppose that Z varies jointly with A and the cube of B, and inversely with the square of C. If $Z = 4$ when $A = 1$, $B = 2$, and $C = 3$, then find Z when $A = 3$, $B = 2$, and $C = 1$.

_____

37. Suppose that F varies jointly with y and the square of z, and inversely with the square of x. If $F = 23$ when $y = 4$, $z = 3$, and $x = 5$, then find F when $y = 2$, $z = 4$, and $x = 3$.

_____

38. Suppose that n varies jointly with r and the square root of w, and inversely with the cube of m. If $n = 19$ when $r = 2$, $w = 4$, and $m = 6$, then find r when $n = 8$, $w = 9$, and $m = 5$.

_____

39. Suppose that Q varies jointly with t and the cube of w, and inversely with m. If $Q = 15$ when $t = 5$, $w = 3$, and $m = 7$, then find t when $Q = 3$, $w = 4$, and $m = 17$.

_____

40. Suppose that S varies jointly with t and the square of w, and inversely with the square of u. If $S = 11$ when $t = 4$, $w = 7$, and $u = 5$, then find t when $S = 1$, $w = 3$, and $u = 2$.

_____

41. Suppose that y varies jointly with the sum of x and z, and inversely with the square of t. If $y = 33.2$ when $t = 4.9$, $x = 1.8$, and $z = 3.8$, then find y when $t = 5.5$, $x = 2.2$, and $z = 3.3$.

_____

Intermediate algebra 2ND Edition

Practice Problem Worksheets

Chapter 6: Radical Expressions

Chapter 6 Section 1: Introduction to Radical Expressions

Problems

1. Find the principal square root of 121.

2. Find the principal square root of 49.

_____

_____

3. Find all the square roots of 169.

4. Find all the square roots of 100.

_____

_____

Find the domain of the given function, for problems 5-8.

5. $f(x) = \sqrt{4 - 2x}$

6. $g(x) = \sqrt{5x - 7}$

_____

_____

7. $h(x) = \sqrt{3 + 5x^2}$

8. $w(x) = \sqrt[3]{2x^2 - 9}$

_____

_____

For problems 9-12, graph the function over the given interval.

9. $f(x) = \sqrt{4 - 2x}$, $[-10, 2]$

10. $g(x) = \sqrt{5x - 7}$, $[0, 10]$

_____

_____

11. $h(x) = \sqrt{3 + 5x^2}$, $[-4, 4]$

12. $Q(x) = \sqrt{2 - x^2}$, $[-1.4, 1.4]$

_____

_____

For problems 13-17, write without radicals, and simplify if possible. (Note: In these problems, x may be negative.)

13. $\sqrt{(2-7x)^2}$

14. $\sqrt{\left(3+8x^2\right)^2}$

_____

_____

15. $\sqrt{\left(5x-4x^2\right)^2}$

16. $\left(\sqrt{1+2x^2}\right)^2$

_____

_____

17. $\left(\sqrt{1+x^2+x^8}\right)^2$

_____

For problems 18-20, graph the function, using the given x values.

18. $y = \sqrt[3]{100x}$,
$x = -10, -\dfrac{5}{4}, -\dfrac{1}{100}, 0, \dfrac{1}{100}, \dfrac{5}{4}, 10$

19. $y = \sqrt[3]{4-x}$, $x = -4, 3, 4, 5, 12$

20. $y = \sqrt[3]{2x+1}$, $x = -14, -1, 0, 13$

_____

For problems 21-30, write without radicals, and simplify if possible. (Note: In these problems, x may be negative.)

21. $\sqrt[5]{(8-x)^5}$

22. $\sqrt[5]{(4x-9)^5}$

23. $\sqrt[6]{(2x-17)^6}$

24. $\sqrt[6]{(8x^2+66x)^6}$

25. $\sqrt[4]{(3x^4+11x^2)^4}$

26. $\sqrt[8]{(99x^8+22y^8)^8}$

27. $\sqrt[4]{(2x^3+3y^5)^4}$

28. $\sqrt[6]{(25x^2-20x+4)^3}$

29. $\sqrt[8]{(x^2+14x+49)^4}$

30. $\sqrt[6]{(x^2-6x+9)^3}$

For problems 31-38, pick the most appropriate inequality (or equality) symbol.

31. $\sqrt[5]{33}$ $\boxed{?}$ $\sqrt[6]{33}$

32. $\sqrt[3]{16}$ $\boxed{?}$ $\sqrt[6]{16}$

33. $\sqrt[9]{\dfrac{15}{11}}$ $\boxed{?}$ $\sqrt[9]{\dfrac{17}{11}}$

34. $\sqrt[3]{\pi}$ $\boxed{?}$ $\sqrt[3]{3}$

35. $\sqrt[11]{10}$ $\boxed{?}$ $\sqrt[10]{10}$

36. $\sqrt[5]{83}$ $\boxed{?}$ $\sqrt[4]{83}$

37. $\sqrt[4]{1.9}$ $\boxed{?}$ $\sqrt[4]{2}$

38. $\sqrt[9]{\dfrac{7}{8}}$ $\boxed{?}$ $\sqrt[9]{\dfrac{3}{8}}$

Chapter 6 Section 2: Radicals and Rational Exponents

Problems

You may assume all variables represent positive quantities, unless noted.

For problems 1-4, rewrite the radical using fractional exponents.

1. $\sqrt[4]{7^3}$

2. $\sqrt[10]{2^7}$

3. $\sqrt[5]{A^4}$

4. $\sqrt[11]{W^{10}}$

For problems 5-8, rewrite using radicals.

5. $3^{\frac{3}{8}}$

6. $7^{\frac{2}{3}}$

7. $x^{\frac{3}{5}}$

8. $Q^{\frac{7}{9}}$

Simplify the expressions in problems 9-14.

9. $\sqrt[6]{4^3}$

10. $\sqrt[3]{24}$

11. $\sqrt[5]{A^{32}}$

12. $\sqrt[7]{x^{50}}$

13. $\sqrt[6]{V^{22}}$

14. $\sqrt[4]{3^{22}}$

Chapter 6 Section 2: Radicals and Rational Exponents

Evaluate the expressions in problems 15-24. Round your answers to the nearest millionth.

15. $\sqrt{99}$

_____

16. $\sqrt[3]{100}$

_____

17. $\sqrt[5]{13}$

_____

18. $\sqrt[7]{111}$

_____

19. $\sqrt[3]{123}$

_____

20. $\sqrt[4]{444}$

_____

21. $\sqrt[5]{235^2}$

_____

22. $\sqrt[10]{1111^3}$

_____

23. $\sqrt[33]{333333^3}$

_____

24. $\sqrt[6]{654^2}$

_____

Simplify problems 25-30 as much as possible.

25. $\sqrt[3]{5}\sqrt[3]{7}$

_____

26. $\sqrt[3]{-4}\sqrt[3]{14}$

_____

27. $\sqrt[5]{-16}\sqrt[5]{-34}$

_____

28. $\sqrt[4]{48}\sqrt[4]{135}$

_____

29. $\dfrac{\sqrt[11]{35}}{\sqrt[11]{7}}$

_____

30. $\dfrac{\sqrt[7]{512}}{\sqrt[7]{-2}}$

_____

Simplify as much as possible, for problems 31-35. For these problems, <u>don't</u> assume that the variables are positive.

31. $\sqrt[4]{A^{12}}$

_____

32. $\sqrt{8x^4}$

_____

33. $\sqrt[4]{16u^4v^8}$

_____

34. $\sqrt{45x^6y^{10}}$

_____

35. $\sqrt{72A^8B^{14}}$

_____

Graph the functions in problems 36-40 over the indicated intervals.

36. $F(x) = \sqrt{10x}$ over [0, 5]

37. $f(x) = \sqrt[3]{x^2}$ over [–10, 10]

_____

_____

38. $h(x) = 1 - \sqrt[5]{2x^3}$ over [–10, 10]

39. $g(x) = 5\sqrt[3]{x^3} - 2x^2$ over [–2, 4]

_____

_____

40. $H(x) = \sqrt[5]{x^9} - 3x$ over [–2, 2]

_____

Problems
For all problems, assume that all variables represent non-negative quantities.

Simplify each expression.

1. $\sqrt{64a^7}$

_____

2. $\sqrt{27x^{22}}$

_____

3. $\sqrt{225x^{17}}$

_____

4. $\sqrt[3]{40y^8}$

_____

5. $\sqrt[3]{270w^{11}}$

_____

6. $\sqrt[3]{280A^4B^7}$

_____

7. $\sqrt[4]{80y^{13}}$

_____

8. $\sqrt{15x^3y^5}\,\sqrt{35x^3y^7}$

_____

9. $\sqrt{12x^3y^2}\,\sqrt{18x^5y^3}$

_____

10. $\sqrt{36x^7y^7}\,\sqrt{27x^4y^5}$

_____

11. $\sqrt[3]{96w^8v^6} \div \sqrt[3]{12w^3v^2}$

_____

12. $\sqrt[3]{750x^{15}y^{18}} \div \sqrt[3]{48x^8y^7}$

_____

For problems 13-20, rewrite the expression under one radical. Simplify the resulting radical expression as much as possible.

13. $\sqrt[5]{x} \cdot \sqrt[7]{x}$

_____

14. $\sqrt{2A^2} \cdot \sqrt[3]{3B}$

_____

15. $\sqrt[4]{4x^3} \cdot \sqrt[3]{3y^2}$

_____

16. $\dfrac{\sqrt[5]{8x^4}}{\sqrt{2x}}$

_____

17. $\sqrt[3]{\sqrt[5]{27x^9}}$

18. $\sqrt{\sqrt[3]{36x^2}}$

___

19. $\sqrt{40x^{11}} \div \sqrt{90x^7}$

20. $\dfrac{\sqrt{225x^{13}}}{\sqrt{36x^8}}$

___

For problems 21-40, rationalize the denominator. Simplify the resulting radical expression as much as possible.

21. $\dfrac{42}{\sqrt{72}}$

22. $\dfrac{x\sqrt{14x}}{\sqrt{35x}}$

___

23. $\dfrac{3x\sqrt{56}}{\sqrt{6x}}$

24. $\dfrac{63x}{\sqrt{7x}}$

___

25. $\dfrac{\sqrt{10x^5y^3}}{xy\sqrt{15xy}}$

26. $\dfrac{\sqrt{40xy^5}}{\sqrt{30x^5y}}$

___

27. $\dfrac{\sqrt{300A^3C^5}}{10A^2C^2\sqrt{3AC}}$

28. $\dfrac{5uv^2\sqrt{3u^7v^3}}{\sqrt{15uv}}$

___

29. $\dfrac{5\sqrt{2}}{\sqrt{3}+\sqrt{2}}$

30. $\dfrac{2\sqrt{5}}{\sqrt{7}-\sqrt{5}}$

___

31. $\dfrac{\sqrt{7} + \sqrt{3}}{\sqrt{7} - \sqrt{3}}$

32. $\dfrac{\sqrt{3x} - \sqrt{x}}{\sqrt{6x} + \sqrt{x}}$

33. $\dfrac{\sqrt{A} + \sqrt{2B}}{\sqrt{2A} + \sqrt{B}}$

34. $\dfrac{\sqrt{6x} - \sqrt{3y}}{\sqrt{3y} - \sqrt{2x}}$

35. $\dfrac{2xy}{\sqrt[3]{4x^2 y^2}}$

36. $2y^2 \sqrt[3]{\dfrac{3x^2}{2y}}$

37. $\dfrac{15xy^2 \sqrt[3]{63x^2 y}}{\sqrt[3]{45xy^2}}$

38. $\dfrac{25}{\sqrt[5]{625}}$

39. $\dfrac{3AB}{\sqrt[5]{81A^3 B^2}}$

40. $\dfrac{2A}{\sqrt[7]{64A^5 B^2}}$

Problems

Simplify each expression. Assume that all variables represent non-negative quantities.

1. $\sqrt{72} + \sqrt{8}$

2. $\sqrt{75} + \sqrt{27}$

3. $\sqrt{252} - \sqrt{175}$

4. $\sqrt{288} - \sqrt{98}$

5. $\sqrt{600} - 3\sqrt{24}$

6. $3\sqrt{147} - 4\sqrt{108} + 5\sqrt{12}$

7. $2\sqrt{72} + \sqrt{800} - 3\sqrt{162}$

8. $\sqrt{27x^7} + 2\sqrt{12x^7}$

9. $2y^2\sqrt{50y^3} + 5\sqrt{18y^7}$

10. $3x\sqrt{27x^3} + 2\sqrt{75x^5} - 4x^2\sqrt{12x}$

11. $2x\sqrt{180x^5} - \sqrt{245x^7}$

12. $5y^2\sqrt{150y^5} + 2y\sqrt{54y^7}$

13. $6x^2\sqrt{132x^2} + 2x\sqrt{297x^4} - x^3\sqrt{3300}$

14. $5u^2\sqrt{24u^3v^5} - 3v\sqrt{54u^7v^3}$

15. $6AB\sqrt{20A^2B^6} - 2B^4\sqrt{45A^4}$

16. $3A^2B^3\sqrt{125A} + 5AB\sqrt{20A^3B^4} - 30B^2\sqrt{5A^5B^2}$

17. $2\sqrt[3]{x^4} - x\sqrt[3]{x}$

18. $4A\sqrt[3]{A^5} - 2A^2\sqrt[3]{A^2}$

19. $3\sqrt[3]{8y^8} + 2y\sqrt[3]{27y^5} - 5y^2\sqrt[3]{8y^2}$

20. $2x^2y^2\sqrt[3]{8x^9y^{11}} + 4y\sqrt[3]{27x^{15}y^{14}}$

21. $x^2 z \sqrt[3]{27x^5 y^7 z^{11}} - 2y \sqrt[3]{x^{11} y^4 z^{14}}$

22. $y \sqrt[3]{64x^{13} y^{11}} + x \sqrt[3]{125x^{10} y^{14}}$

_____

23. $2\sqrt[4]{16x^9} - 3x \sqrt[4]{x^5}$

24. $5A \sqrt[4]{512A^5} - 9A^2 \sqrt[4]{32A}$

_____

25. $5\sqrt[4]{16y^{10}} + 2y \sqrt[4]{81y^6}$

26. $6u^2 v \sqrt[4]{80u^5 v^7} - 10u \sqrt[4]{5u^9 v^{11}}$

_____

27. $7x \sqrt[4]{2xy^5 z^{10}} + 2yz \sqrt[4]{32x^5 yz^6}$

28. $2\sqrt[5]{32x^9} - 3x \sqrt[5]{x^4}$

_____

29. $3A \sqrt[5]{256A^8} - 4\sqrt[5]{8A^{13}}$

30. $y \sqrt[5]{64x^{24} y^{12}} + x \sqrt[5]{2x^{19} y^{17}}$

_____

31. $2x^2 y \sqrt[5]{32x^2 y} - x \sqrt[5]{243x^7 y^6}$

32. $4u^2 v \sqrt[5]{64u^{16} v^{23}} + u^4 v^4 \sqrt[5]{2u^6 v^8}$

_____

33. $6xy \sqrt[10]{x^{42} y^{71}} + 3 \sqrt[10]{x^{52} y^{81}}$

34. $3AC^2 \sqrt[10]{A^{42} B^{71} C^{73}} - 2A^2 B^5 C \sqrt[10]{A^{32} B^{21} C^{83}}$

_____

35. $3x^3 y^2 \sqrt[10]{x^{28} y^{59}} - 2xy^4 \sqrt[10]{x^{48} y^{39}}$

36. $4AB^3 \sqrt[10]{2^{20} \cdot 9A^{34} B^{17}} - 2A^3 \sqrt[10]{3^{12} A^{14} B^{47}}$

_____

37. $\sqrt[3]{9 \sqrt[4]{81x^2}} + \sqrt[4]{27 \sqrt[3]{27x^2}}$

38. $\sqrt{18 \sqrt[3]{8x}} - 2\sqrt[3]{4 \sqrt{4x}}$

_____

39. $\sqrt[3]{125 \sqrt{x}} - \sqrt{16 \sqrt[3]{x}}$

40. $3\sqrt[3]{8 \sqrt[5]{x^4}} - \sqrt[5]{32 \sqrt[3]{x^4}}$

_____

Problems

Solve each radical equation.

1. $\sqrt{x} = 12$

2. $\sqrt{3x} = 15$

_____

3. $8 = \sqrt{7x}$

4. $2 - \sqrt{W} = -3$

_____

5. $8 - 2\sqrt{x} = 5$

6. $7 - 4\sqrt{2x} = 6$

_____

7. $5\sqrt{t - 20} = -12$

8. $3\sqrt{y - 10} = 20$

_____

9. $\sqrt{8x - 7} = x$

10. $\sqrt{4x^2 + x} = 2x + 1$

_____

11. $3x = 4\sqrt{5x - 4}$

12. $5 - 4\sqrt{t} = 2\sqrt{t} + 2$

_____

13. $\sqrt{4w - 1} = 3\sqrt{w + 1}$

14. $3\sqrt{5x} = 2\sqrt{2x + 1}$

_____

15. $3\sqrt{2x + 1} = 2\sqrt{3x - 1}$

16. $\sqrt{3u - 8} + \sqrt{7u + 1} = 0$

_____

17. $\sqrt{5x - 2} + 2\sqrt{2x - 5} = 0$

18. $\sqrt{5x^2 + 4x + 2} = \sqrt{4x^2 + 7}$

_____

19. $\sqrt{10x^2 - 10x + 9} = 3\sqrt{x^2 - 10x + 1}$

20. $\sqrt{6z - 7} + \sqrt{4z - 9} = 0$

_____

21. $\sqrt{x+8} - \sqrt{x-1} = 1$

22. $\sqrt{y+5} - 2\sqrt{y} = 1$

_____

23. $\sqrt{x+2} = 2 - 3\sqrt{x-2}$

24. $\sqrt{x+6} = 1 + \sqrt{x+4}$

_____

25. $\sqrt{y-10} - \sqrt{y-12} = 1$

26. $\sqrt{x+2} - 4 = \sqrt{x-6}$

_____

27. $\sqrt[3]{3u-1} + 2 = 5$

28. $\sqrt[3]{2x+4} - 3 = 0$

_____

29. $\sqrt[3]{7-3t} = 2$

30. $2 - \sqrt[4]{x^2 + 10x + 25} = 1$

_____

31. $\sqrt[4]{r^2 - 18r + 81} - 4 = 0$

32. $\sqrt[3]{s^2} + 3\sqrt[3]{s} - 40 = 0$

_____

33. $\sqrt[3]{x^2} - 9\sqrt[3]{x} + 20 = 0$

34. $y^{\frac{2}{5}} - 6y^{\frac{1}{5}} + 5 = 0$

_____

35. $x^{\frac{4}{3}} - 4x^{\frac{2}{3}} - 21 = 0$

36. $t^{\frac{2}{3}} - 8t^{\frac{1}{3}} + 15 = 0$

_____

37. $u^{\frac{5}{3}} - 10^5 = 0$

38. $x^{\frac{5}{7}} + 32 = 0$

_____

39. $w^{\frac{3}{4}} - 2 = 0$

40. $y^{\frac{3}{5}} = 5$

_____

Problems

1. $(1 + 2i) + (3 + 4i) = ?$

2. $(35 + 73i) + (52 + 3i) = ?$

_____

3. $(2 - 9i) + (-2 + i) = ?$

4. $(5 - 3i) + (-6 + 8i) = ?$

_____

5. $(30 + 13i) + (32 - 5i) = ?$

6. $(20 - 7i) - (-10 - 6i) = ?$

_____

7. $(-6 + 3i) - (-7 + 2i) = ?$

8. $(3 + 8i) - (-8 + 3i) = ?$

_____

9. $(18 + 13i) - (12 + 5i) = ?$

10. $(5 + 2i)(2 + 8i) = ?$

_____

11. $(-2 - 9i)(9 - 2i) = ?$

12. $(5 - 3i)(2 - 6i) = ?$

_____

13. $(2 + 3i)(4 + 5i) = ?$

14. $(8 + 3i)(3 + 5i) = ?$

_____

15. $(6 + 7i)(-2 + 3i) = ?$

16. $(5 - 7i)(5 + 7i) = ?$

_____

17. $(1 + 8i)(1 - 8i) = ?$

18. $(-2 - i)(-2 + i) = ?$

_____

19. $(2 - 6i)(2 + 6i) = ?$

20. $(5 - 4i)(5 + 4i) = ?$

_____

21. $\dfrac{7 + 2i}{2 + 5i} = ?$

22. $\dfrac{-2 + 3i}{1 + 2i} = ?$

_____

23. $\dfrac{1 + 2i}{2 - i} = ?$

24. $\dfrac{-3 + 5i}{5 + 3i} = ?$

_____

25. $\dfrac{-1 + 3i}{-1 + 4i} = ?$

26. $\dfrac{6 + 4i}{2 - 2i} = ?$

_____

27. $\dfrac{2 - i}{1 - i} = ?$

28. $\dfrac{3 - 2i}{5 + 3i} = ?$

_____

29. $\dfrac{-9 + 2i}{1 - 2i} = ?$

30. $\dfrac{3 + i}{6 - 5i} = ?$

_____

31. Write $\sqrt{-7}$ as an imaginary number.

32. Write $\sqrt{-50}$ as an imaginary number.

_____

33. Write $\sqrt{-200}$ as an imaginary number.

34. Write $-\sqrt{-147}$ as an imaginary number.

_____

35. $i^{28} = ?$

36. $i^{149} = ?$

_____

37. $i^{251} = ?$

38. $i^{1234} = ?$

_____

39. $i^{-42} = ?$

40. $i^{-169} = ?$

_____

Intermediate Algebra 2ⁿᵈ Edition

Practice Problem Worksheets

Chapter 7: Quadratic Equations and Inequalities

Chapter 7 Section 1: Quadratic Equations

Problems

Solve each equation, for problems 1-10.

1. $(3x-1)^2 = 4$

2. $(7x+4)^2 = 7$

_____

3. $(4x-3)^2 = 9$

4. $(2x+5)^2 = 10$

_____

5. $(5x-2)^2 = 3$

6. $(3x-1)^2 + 2 = 0$

_____

7. $(5x+1)^2 - 4 = 0$

8. $(4x-5)^2 + 3 = 0$

_____

9. $(7x+4)^2 - 5 = 0$

10. $(6x+11)^2 + 8 = 0$

_____

In problems 11-15, complete the square by filling in the blanks.

11. $x^2 + 10x + \square = (x + \square)^2$

12. $x^2 + 6x + \square = (x + \square)^2$

_____

13. $x^2 - 8x + \square = (x - \square)^2$

14. $x^2 - 7x + \square = (x - \square)^2$

_____

15. $x^2 + 5x + \square = (x + \square)^2$

_____

Solve problems 16-33 by completing the square.

16. $x^2 - 4x - 7 = 0$

17. $x^2 - 10x - 1 = 0$

_____

_____

18. $x^2 + 6x + 3 = 0$

19. $x^2 - 7x + 9 = 0$

_____

_____

20. $x^2 + 9x + 4 = 0$

21. $x^2 + 8x + 13 = 0$

_____

_____

22. $x^2 - x = -1$

23. $x(x + 5) + 8 = 0$

_____

_____

24. $x(3x - 2) = 4$

25. $2x(x + 3) = -3$

_____

_____

26. $5x^2 + 7x + 3 = 0$

27. $2(x^2 + 2) = -9x$

_____

_____

28. $3x^2 + 4x + 10 = 0$

29. $6x^2 + 1 = x$

_____

_____

30. $x(2x + 5) = 8$

31. $3x(x - 1) = 2$

_____

_____

32. $2x(x + 1) = 3(x - 2)$

33. $x^2 + 3x(x + 2) = 3(4 - 2x)$

_____

_____

Find the x-intercepts of the parabola defined by the equation in problems 34-40.

34. $y = 2x^2 + 4x - 7$

35. $y = x^2 + 8x - 1$

_____

36. $y = x^2 - 6x - 8$

37. $y = 3x^2 - 9x + 5$

_____

38. $y = 2x^2 - 4x - 8$

39. $y = 3x^2 - 2x + 7$

_____

40. $y = 4x^2 - 20x + 25$

_____

Chapter 7 Section 2: The Quadratic Formula

Problems
NOTE: Round to the nearest millionth, where appropriate.

1. Find the exact solutions, using radicals, to the equation $x^2 + 9x - 2 = 0$.

2. Find the exact solutions, using radicals, to the equation $x^2 + 10x + 13 = 0$.

3. Find the exact solutions, using radicals, to the equation $x^2 - 2x - 11 = 0$.

4. Find approximate decimal solutions to the equation $x^2 - 11x + 3 = 0$.

5. Find approximate decimal solutions to the equation $x(3x + 8) = 10$.

6. Find approximate decimal solutions to the equation $x(5x - 11) = 2$.

7. Find the exact solutions, using radicals, to the equation $x(7x + 1) = 5$.

8. Find the exact solutions, using radicals, to the equation $x(9 - x) = 1$.

9. Find the exact solutions to the equation: $x^2 - 5\left(x^2 - 2\right) = 3x\left(x - 1\right)$.

10. Find the exact solutions to the equation: $x^2 - 2\left(x^2 - 7\right) = x\left(x + 2\right)$.

11. Find approximate decimal solutions to the equation $x^2 + 3\left(x^2 - 1\right) = 2x\left(x + 1\right)$.

12. Find the solution to the equation $x^2 + 2\left(x^2 - 6\right) = 6x\left(x + 2\right)$.

13. Find approximate decimal solutions to the equation $\dfrac{1}{x^2} - \dfrac{5}{x} = 2$.

14. Find the exact solutions, using radicals, to the equation $\dfrac{3}{x^2} - \dfrac{1}{x} = 7$.

15. Find the solutions to the equation $\dfrac{8}{x^2} + \dfrac{3}{x} = 5$.

16. Find the exact solutions, using radicals, to the equation $\dfrac{4}{x^2} = 6 + \dfrac{1}{x}$.

17. Find the exact solutions, using radicals, to the equation $\dfrac{1}{x+2} + \dfrac{1}{x} = \dfrac{1}{3}$.

18. Find the solutions to the equation $\dfrac{5}{x-1} - \dfrac{3}{x} = \dfrac{1}{2}$.

19. Find the exact solutions, using radicals, to the equation $\dfrac{1}{x-2} - \dfrac{1}{x} = \dfrac{1}{5}$.

20. Find the exact solutions, using radicals, to the equation $\dfrac{4}{x-3} - \dfrac{4}{x+3} = 1$.

21. Find the exact solution to the equation $\dfrac{1}{x-5} + \dfrac{1}{x+5} = \dfrac{2}{x^2-25}$.

22. Find the exact solutions to the equation $\dfrac{3}{x-2} - \dfrac{2}{x+3} = \dfrac{1}{x^2+x-6}$.

23. Solve $\sqrt[3]{t^2} - \sqrt[3]{t} = 4$.

24. Solve $\sqrt[3]{t^2} + 6\sqrt[3]{t} = 6$.

25. Solve $\sqrt[5]{u^2} = 5 - 2\sqrt[5]{u}$.

26. Solve $\left(\sqrt[3]{t+2}\right)^2 + 2\sqrt[3]{t+2} = 2$.

27. Solve $\left(\sqrt[4]{w-1}\right)^2 + 4\sqrt[4]{w-1} = 6$.

28. Solve $5x(1+x) = 4 + x^2$.

29. Solve $2x(x-3) = 8 + x^2$.

30. Solve $4x(5+x) = 1 + x^2$.

31. Find the equation of the line of symmetry (i.e., the *axis*) of the parabola defined by the equation: $y = 5x^2 - 60x - 101$.

32. Find the equation of the line of symmetry (i.e., the *axis*) of the parabola defined by the equation: $y = 8x^2 + 48x - 27$.

33. Find the equation of the line of symmetry (i.e., the *axis*) of the parabola defined by the equation: $y = 7x^2 + 70x + 17$.

_____

34. Find the coordinates of the vertex of the parabola: $y = 3x^2 - 12x + 23$; also state whether the vertex is a maximum or minimum.

_____

35. Find the coordinates of the vertex of the parabola: $y = -7x^2 + 98x - 340$; also state whether the vertex is a maximum or minimum.

_____

36. Find the coordinates of the vertex of the parabola: $y = -x^2 + 6x - 8$; also state whether the vertex is a maximum or minimum.

_____

37. Find the coordinates of the vertex of the parabola: $y = 5x^2 - 30x + 50$; also state whether the vertex is a maximum or minimum.

_____

38. Find the maximum output of the function $f(u) = u(6 - u) + 3$.

_____

39. Find the minimum output of the function $g(x) = x^2 - 10x + 27$.

_____

40. Find the maximum output of the function $h(t) = -3t^2 - 36t - 100$.

_____

Problems

Graph each quadratic function.

1. $f(x) = 3x^2 - 6x - 2$

2. $g(x) = 2x^2 - 8x + 3$

3. $h(x) = -3x^2 - 18x - 1$

4. $F(x) = -2x^2 + 10x + 7$

5. $G(x) = x^2 - 4x + 2$

6. $H(x) = -3x^2 + 18x + 4$

7. $f(x) = -x^2 - 6x + 10$

8. $g(x) = 5x^2 + 30x - 9$

9. $h(x) = -2x^2 + 5x$

10. $F(x) = 4x^2 + 16x - 52$

_____

11. $G(x) = 2x^2 - 3$

12. $H(x) = -3x^2 + 2$

_____

13. $f(x) = 5x^2 - 2x$

14. $g(x) = -4x^2 + x - 1$

_____

15. $h(x) = 5x^2 + 10x - 5$

16. $F(x) = -5x^2 + 5x + 10$

_____

17. $G(x) = x^2 + 6x - 2$

18. $H(x) = -x^2 + 8x + 1$

_____

19. $f(x) = 6x^2 + 24x$

20. $g(x) = 3x^2 + 1$

_____

_____

21. $h(x) = -3x^2 + 6x + 2$

22. $F(x) = -2x^2 + 8x - 3$

_____

_____

23. $G(x) = 3x^2 + 18x + 1$

24. $H(x) = 2x^2 - 10x - 7$

_____

_____

25. $f(x) = -x(x-4) - 2$

26. $g(x) = 3x(x-6) - 4$

_____

_____

27. $h(x) = x(x+6) - 10$

28. $F(x) = -5x(x+6) + 9$

_____

_____

29. $G(x) = x(2x - 5)$

30. $H(x) = -4x(x + 4) + 52$

---

31. $f(x) = -2x^2 + 3$

32. $g(x) = 3x^2 - 2$

---

33. $h(x) = x(2 - 5x)$

34. $F(x) = x(4x - 1) + 1$

---

35. $G(x) = -5(-1 + x(x + 2))$

36. $H(x) = 5(-2 + x(x - 1))$

---

37. $f(x) = 2 - x(x + 6)$

38. $g(x) = x(x - 8) - 1$

---

39. $h(x) = -6x(x+4)$

40. $F(x) = -\left(3x^2 + 1\right)$

_____   _____

Chapter 7 Section 4: Applications of Quadratic Equations

Problems

Note: Problems 1-17 use the projectile equation $h = -16.1t^2 + v_0 t + h_0$, where h is the height of the projectile after t seconds, v_0 is the initial velocity of the projectile, and h_0 is the initial height of the projectile. (in feet)

1. A baseball is thrown straight up into the air with an initial velocity of 120 feet per second, from a height of 4 feet. How high is the ball after 4 seconds, to the nearest tenth of a foot?

    _____

2. A baseball is thrown straight up into the air with an initial velocity of 120 feet per second, from a height of 4 feet. How high is the ball after 5 seconds, to the nearest tenth of a foot?

    _____

3. A rock is thrown straight up into the air with an initial velocity of 90 feet per second, from a height of 6 feet. How high is the rock after 2 seconds, to the nearest tenth of a foot?

    _____

4. A rock is thrown straight up into the air with an initial velocity of 90 feet per second, from a height of 6 feet. How high is the rock after 4 seconds, to the nearest tenth of a foot?

    _____

5. An object is thrown straight down with an initial velocity of 50 feet per second, from a height of 500 feet. How high is the object after 4 seconds, to the nearest tenth of a foot?
    (Hint: use $v_0 = -50$, since it's being thrown *down* rather than up.)

    _____

6. An object is thrown straight down with an initial velocity of 70 feet per second, from a height of 1,000 feet. How high is the object after 6 seconds, to the nearest tenth of a foot?
    (Hint: use $v_0 = -70$, since it's being thrown *down* rather than up.)

    _____

7. A rock is dropped off a 3,100 foot cliff. How long will it take the rock to fall to the bottom of the cliff? (Round your answer to the nearest tenth of a second.)

    _____

8. An object is dropped off a 4,000 foot cliff. How long will it take the object to fall to the bottom of the cliff? (Round your answer to the nearest tenth of a second.)

    _____

9. A rock is dropped off a 10,000 foot cliff. How long will it take the rock to fall to the bottom of the cliff? (Round your answer to the nearest tenth of a second.)

    _____

10. An object is dropped into a 1,200 foot ravine. How long will it take the object to fall to the bottom of the ravine? (Round your answer to the nearest tenth of a second.)

_____

11. A rock is dropped into an 800 foot ravine. How long will it take the rock to fall to the bottom of the ravine? (Round your answer to the nearest tenth of a second.)

_____

12. A projectile is shot straight up with an initial velocity of 100 feet per second. How high will it go, to the nearest tenth of a foot?

_____

13. A projectile is shot straight up with an initial velocity of 200 feet per second. How high will it go, to the nearest tenth of a foot?

_____

14. A projectile is shot straight up with an initial velocity of 120 feet per second, from an initial height of 200 feet. How high will it go, to the nearest tenth of a foot?

_____

15. A baseball is thrown straight up into the air, with an initial velocity of 120 feet per second, from a height of 4 feet. How high will the ball go, to the nearest tenth of a foot?

_____

16. A rock is dropped down a well. It takes 4 seconds to hear the splash. Approximately how deep is the well, to the nearest foot?

_____

17. A rock is dropped down a well. It takes 3 seconds to hear the splash. Approximately how deep is the well, to the nearest foot?

_____

18. Suppose the profit, P, as a function of the number of widgets, n, a factory produces per year is given by

$$P = -15n^2 + 4020n.$$

How many widgets should the factory produce each year to yield the maximum profit, and what is the maximum profit?

_____

19. Suppose the profit, P, as a function of the number of gadgets, n, a factory produces per year is given by $P = -25n^2 + 1000n$. How many gadgets should the factory produce each year to yield the maximum profit, and what is the maximum profit?

_____

20. Suppose the profit, P, as a function of the number of robots, n, a factory produces per month is given by $P = -10n^2 + 5000n$. How many robots should the factory produce each month to maximize their profit, and what is the maximum profit?

_____

21. Suppose the profit, P, as a function of the number of robots, n, a factory produces per month is given by $P = -20n^2 + 6000n$. How many robots should the factory produce each month to maximize their profit, and what is the maximum profit?

_____

22. Suppose the profit, P, as a function of the number of robots, n, a factory produces per month is given by $P = -50n^2 + 50000n$. How many robots should the factory produce each month to maximize their profit, and what is the maximum profit?

_____

23. Suppose you want to build a rectangular pen alongside your house for a puppy. A side of your house will serve as one side of the pen, and you have 30 feet of fencing to use for the other three sides of the rectangular pen. What is the maximum area of the enclosure?

_____

24. Suppose you want to build a rectangular boat house alongside a river. The river will serve as one side of the boat house, and you have 500 feet of fencing to use for the other three sides of the rectangular structure. What is the maximum area of the boat house?

_____

25. Suppose you want to build a rectangular storage box. Suppose that one edge of its base is x cm long, and the other edge is $x^2 - 20x + 110$ cm long. Also suppose the height is $10/x$ cm long. What is the maximum possible volume of the box?

_____

26. Suppose you want to build a rectangular storage box. Suppose that one edge of its base is x cm long, and the other edge is $x^2 - 10x + 100$ cm long. Also suppose the height is $2/x$ cm long. What is the maximum possible volume of the box?

_____

Problems 27-30 refer to this structure:

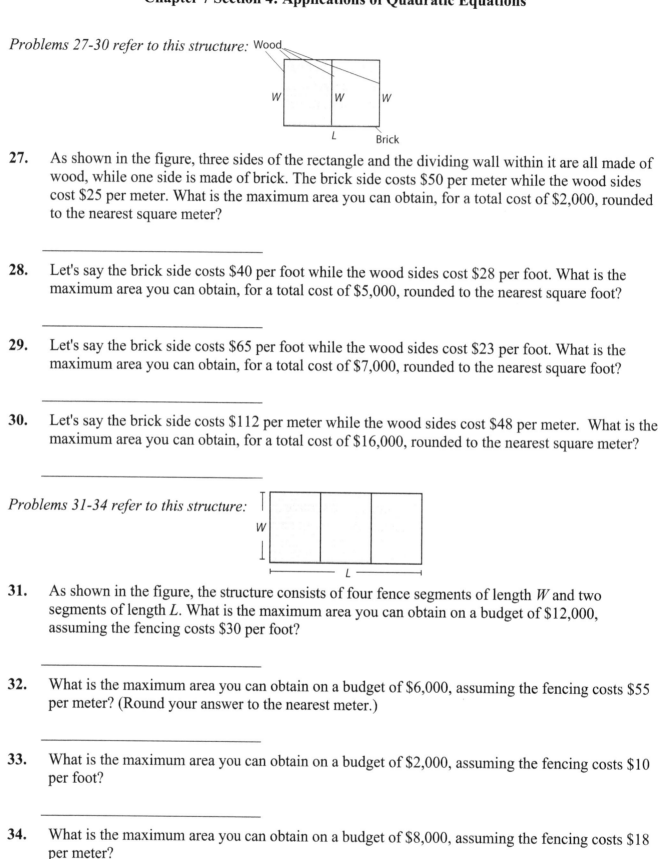

27. As shown in the figure, three sides of the rectangle and the dividing wall within it are all made of wood, while one side is made of brick. The brick side costs $50 per meter while the wood sides cost $25 per meter. What is the maximum area you can obtain, for a total cost of $2,000, rounded to the nearest square meter?

_____

28. Let's say the brick side costs $40 per foot while the wood sides cost $28 per foot. What is the maximum area you can obtain, for a total cost of $5,000, rounded to the nearest square foot?

_____

29. Let's say the brick side costs $65 per foot while the wood sides cost $23 per foot. What is the maximum area you can obtain, for a total cost of $7,000, rounded to the nearest square foot?

_____

30. Let's say the brick side costs $112 per meter while the wood sides cost $48 per meter. What is the maximum area you can obtain, for a total cost of $16,000, rounded to the nearest square meter?

_____

Problems 31-34 refer to this structure:

31. As shown in the figure, the structure consists of four fence segments of length W and two segments of length L. What is the maximum area you can obtain on a budget of $12,000, assuming the fencing costs $30 per foot?

_____

32. What is the maximum area you can obtain on a budget of $6,000, assuming the fencing costs $55 per meter? (Round your answer to the nearest meter.)

_____

33. What is the maximum area you can obtain on a budget of $2,000, assuming the fencing costs $10 per foot?

_____

34. What is the maximum area you can obtain on a budget of $8,000, assuming the fencing costs $18 per meter?

_____

Problems 35-38 refer to the following structure:

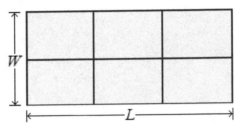

35. As shown in the figure, the structure consists of four fence segments of length W and three segments of length L. What is the maximum area you can obtain on a budget of $10,000, assuming the fencing costs $20 per meter?

    _____

36. What is the maximum area you can obtain on a budget of $6,000, assuming the fencing costs $6 per foot?

    _____

37. What is the maximum area you can obtain on a budget of $8,000, assuming the fencing costs $40 per meter?

    _____

38. What is the maximum area you can obtain on a budget of $10,000, assuming the fencing costs $35 per meter?

    _____

Chapter 7 Section 5: Polynomial and Rational Inequalities

Problems

For each problem, graph the solution set of the given inequality, and then express your solution in both interval notation and in set-builder notation.

1. $(x-3)(x-8) > 0$

2. $(x-2)(x-10) > 0$

3. $(x-1)(x+5) < 0$

4. $(x-5)(x+7) < 0$

5. $x^2 - 2x - 24 \geq 0$

6. $x^2 - 13x + 22 \geq 0$

7. $x^2 - 15x + 56 \leq 0$

8. $x^2 + 20x + 99 \leq 0$

9. $x^2 + x > 72$

10. $x^2 + 2x > 48$

179

11. $x^2 - 9x \leq 22$

12. $x^2 + 3x \leq 88$

---

13. $x(x+1) \geq 30$

14. $x(x+1) \geq 20$

---

15. $x(x-2) < 35$

16. $x(x+12) < 13$

---

17. $(x+2)(x-4)(x-1) > 0$

18. $(x+1)(x-2)(x+3) > 0$

---

19. $(x+3)(x+6)(x-4) \leq 0$

20. $x(x-5)(x+2) \leq 0$

---

21. $\dfrac{(x+3)(x+6)}{x-4} > 0$

22. $\dfrac{(x-2)(x+7)}{x-5} > 0$

---

23. $\dfrac{x+3}{(x+1)(x+5)} < 0$

24. $\dfrac{x-5}{x^2-3x-88} \geq 0$

---

25. $\dfrac{x^2+12x+32}{x+3} \geq 0$

26. $\dfrac{(x+1)(x-1)}{(x-2)(x+2)} > 0$

---

27. $\dfrac{x^2-9x-36}{x^2+9x-36} < 0$

28. $\dfrac{x^2-11x+28}{x^2+5x-24} \leq 0$

---

29. $(3-x)(x-4) > 0$

30. $x^2+5x-50 \geq 0$

---

31. $x^2-14x+24 \leq 0$

32. $(5-x)(x+8) < 0$

---

33. $x^2 + 5x > 66$

34. $x(x - 21) \geq -20$

_____

_____

35. $x^2 + 10x \leq 39$

36. $x(x - 14) < -48$

_____

_____

37. $(x + 3)(1 - x)(x + 5) > 0$

38. $x(1 - x)(x + 7) \leq 0$

_____

_____

39. $\dfrac{(6 - x)(x + 2)}{x - 4} > 0$

40. $\dfrac{(5 - x)(x + 3)}{x + 8} \leq 0$

_____

_____

Intermediate Algebra 2ND Edition

Practice Problem Worksheets

<u>Chapter 8: Exponentials and Logarithms</u>

Problems

1. Find the domain of the function
$F = \{ (1,5), (3,7), (5,1), (6,2) \}$.

2. Find the range of the function
$F = \{ (1,5), (3,7), (5,1), (6,2) \}$.

_____

_____

3. Find the domain of the function
$G = \{ (2,1), (3,6), (7,1), (8,6), (11,1) \}$.

4. Find the range of the function
$G = \{ (2,1), (3,6), (7,1), (8,6), (11,1) \}$.

_____

_____

For problems 5-35, decide whether or not the given function is invertible; if so, find its inverse.

5. $f = \{ (1,2), (2,3), (3,1) \}$

6. $g = \{ (1,3), (2,4), (3,2), (4,1) \}$

_____

_____

7. $h = \{ (1,3), (2,5), (3,4), (4,1), (5,2) \}$

8. $W = \{ (1,2), (2,3), (3,4), (4,3) \}$

_____

_____

9. $F = \{ (1,6), (2,6), (3,4), (4,3), (5,2), (6,1) \}$

10. $Q = \{ (1,6), (2,5), (3,4), (4,3), (5,2), (6,1) \}$

_____

_____

11. $G = \{(1,3), (2,1), (3,7), (4,5), (5,6), (6,4), (7,3)\}$

12. $M = \{(1,3), (2,1), (3,7), (4,5), (5,6), (6,4)\}$

_____

_____

13. $L(x) = 2x + 3$

14. $I(x) = 5x - 7$

_____

_____

15. $g(t) = 5t^2 - 7$

16. $h(x) = x^4 - 5x^2 + 2$

_____

_____

17. $f(u) = 8u - 1$

18. $T(w) = \dfrac{4w + 9}{5}$

_____

_____

19. $h(x) = x^2 + 3$

20. $T(t) = t^2 + 3t - 9$

_____

_____

21. $g(x) = x^3 - 1$

22. $M(x) = x^3 + 11$

_____

_____

23. $F(v) = 5v^2 - 3v + 20$

24. $P(x) = 4x^2 + x - 1$

_____

_____

25. $L(x) = 10x - 13$

26. $g(x) = 6 - 17x$

_____

_____

27. $h(t) = 6 + 6t^6$

28. $G(t) = \dfrac{t - 3}{1 - t}$

_____

_____

29. $H(x) = \dfrac{x^2 - 3}{2 - x^2}$

30. $V(x) = \dfrac{x^4 + 7}{2x^6 - 1}$

_____

_____

31. $f(x) = \dfrac{3x}{x - 7}$

32. $g(x) = \dfrac{x - 5}{x + 1}$

_____

_____

33. $h(x) = \dfrac{2x^4}{x^2 - 3}$

34. $k(x) = \dfrac{x + 6}{x}$

_____

_____

35. $f(x) = \dfrac{x}{x + 6}$

_____

For problems 36-40, graph each function along with its inverse function and the line $y = x$.

36. $L(x) = 5x - 9$

37. $M(x) = \dfrac{2}{3}x - 2$

_____   _____

38. $G(x) = 8x^3 - 7$

39. $H(x) = \dfrac{-1}{x+1}$

_____   _____

40. $f(x) = \dfrac{x-2}{x+3}$

_____

41. If $f(x) = 1 - 5x$ and $g(x) = x^2$,

then $(f \circ g)(x) = ?$

42. If $f(x) = x - 5$ and $g(x) = 2x^2$,

then $(f \circ g)(x) = ?$

43. If $f(x) = 1 - 5x$ and $g(x) = x^2$,

then $(g \circ f)(x) = ?$

44. If $f(x) = \dfrac{2}{x}$ and $g(x) = 3x^5$, then

$(g \circ f)(x) = ?$

45. If $f(x) = \dfrac{x}{x+1}$ and $g(x) = x^3$,

then $(g \circ f)(x) = ?$

46. If $f(x) = \dfrac{2}{x}$ and $g(x) = 3x^5$, then

$(f \circ g)(x) = ?$

47. If $f(x) = \dfrac{x}{x+1}$ and $g(x) = x^3$,

then $(f \circ g)(x) = ?$

48. If $f(x) = \dfrac{x-9}{x+19}$ and $g(x) = x^4$,

then $(f \circ g)(x) = ?$

Problems

For problems 1-20, graph the given exponential function.

1. $f(x) = 5^x$

2. $g(x) = 1.1^x$

_____   _____

3. $h(x) = 3^x$

4. $r(x) = 10^x$

_____   _____

5. $v(x) = \pi^x$

6. $F(x) = 5^{-x}$

_____   _____

7. $G(x) = 1.1^{-x}$

8. $H(x) = 3^{-x}$

_____   _____

9. $R(x) = 10^{-x}$

10. $V(x) = \pi^{-x}$

_____

_____

11. $f(t) = 3 \cdot 2^{\frac{t}{4}}$

12. $g(x) = 2 \cdot 5^{\frac{x}{7}}$

_____

_____

13. $h(t) = 10 \cdot 3^{-\frac{t}{2}}$

14. $w(x) = 5\left(\sqrt{2}\right)^{x}$

_____

_____

15. $M(t) = 2\left(\sqrt{2}\right)^{\frac{t}{2}}$

16. $P(x) = 2 \cdot 3^{x-3}$

_____

_____

17. $Q(t) = 3 \cdot 2^{t-1}$

18. $W(x) = 3\left(\sqrt{3}\right)^{x-3}$

---

19. $V(x) = 3 \cdot 2^{\frac{x-2}{3}}$

20. $R(t) = \pi \cdot 3^{\frac{x-1}{2}}$

Problems 21-30 all involve the formula for compound interest. If A_0 dollars are invested at annual interest rate r, compounded monthly, then after t years the account will have grown to

$$A(t) = A_0\left(1 + \frac{r}{12}\right)^{12t}.$$

21. If \$1000 is placed into an account earning 6% annual interest, compounded monthly, how much will it grow to after 10 years?

---

22. If \$1000 is placed into an account earning 8% annual interest, compounded monthly, how much will it grow to after 10 years?

---

23. If \$5000 is placed into an account earning 5% annual interest, compounded monthly, how much will it grow to after 50 years?

---

24. If \$200 is placed into an account earning 10% annual interest, compounded monthly, how much will it grow to after 20 years?

---

25. If $3000 is placed into an account earning 50% annual interest, compounded monthly, how much will it grow to after 5 years?

   _____

26. Legend has it that Manhattan Island was "purchased" from the Indians in 1626 for $24 worth of glass beads. If that amount were invested in an account earning 6% annual interest, compounded monthly, how much would it have grown to by the year 2004? Round off your answer to the nearest million.

   _____

27. Your future self comes to you in a dream, revealing that a certain stock will earn a 30% annual interest rate (compounded monthly). How much will a $10,000 investment in this stock grow to in 20 years?

   _____

28. Imagine that you invested $5,000 in the initial public offering of Microsoft stock in 1986. How much will it have grown to by the year 2006? Assume that it will earn 31% annual interest, compounded monthly.

   _____

29. Your future self comes to you in a dream, revealing that a certain stock will earn a 40% annual interest rate (compounded monthly). How much will a $2,000 investment in this stock grow to in 20 years?

   _____

30. Imagine that your friend invested $10,000 in the initial public offering of Microsoft stock in 1986. How much would it have grown to by the year 2001? Assume that it earned an annual interest of 32%, compounded monthly.

   _____

Problems 31-40 all involve the formula

$$A(t) = A_0 e^{rt}.$$

This same equation is used for unconstrained population growth, continuous compounding of interest, and radioactive decay. In each case, A_0 is the initial amount at time $t = 0$, and r is the growth rate per unit of time. For radioactive decay problems, r is negative. Sometimes, P and P_0 are used in place of A and A_0 for population-related problems, but the equation used is still the same one.

31. A population of bacteria is modeled by the equation
$$A(t) = 1000e^{0.4t}$$
where t is measured in hours. How many bacteria will there be after five hours have elapsed?

_____

32. A population of bacteria is modeled by the equation
$$A(t) = 200e^{0.6t}$$
where t is measured in hours. How many bacteria will there be after four hours have elapsed?

_____

33. A population of bacteria is modeled by the equation
$$A(t) = 100e^{0.9t}$$
where t is measured in hours. How many bacteria will there be after sixteen hours have elapsed?

_____

34. If you invest \$5,000 earning an annual interest rate of 7%, compounded continuously, then after t years, your investment will grow to
$$A(t) = 5000e^{0.07t}.$$
How much will the account have grown to after 10 years?

_____

35. If you invest \$12,345 earning an annual interest rate of 9%, compounded continuously, then after t years, your investment will grow to
$$A(t) = 12345e^{0.09t}.$$
How much will the account have grown to after 15 years?

_____

36. If you invest \$20,000 earning an annual interest rate of 10%, compounded continuously, then after t years, your investment will grow to
$$A(t) = 20000e^{0.1t}.$$
How much will the account have grown to after 10 years?

_____

In problems 37-40, round your answer to the nearest thousandth of a gram.

37. The amount (in grams) of a radioactive substance left after t years is modeled by the equation:
$$A(t) = 10e^{-0.13t}$$
How much of the initial 10 gram sample will remain after 5 years?

_____

38. The amount (in grams) of a radioactive substance left after t years is modeled by the equation:
$$A(t) = 50e^{-0.21t}$$
How much of the initial 50 gram sample will remain after 10 years?

_____

39. The amount (in grams) of a radioactive substance left after t years is modeled by the equation:
$$A(t) = 25e^{-0.37t}$$
How much of the initial 25 gram sample will remain after 15 years?

_____

40. The amount (in grams) of a Cesium-137 left after t years is modeled by the equation:
$$A(t) = 50e^{-0.0231t}$$
How much will remain after 10 years?

_____

Problems

In problems 1-5, write the exponential equation in logarithmic form.

1. $y = 9^x$

   _____

2. $t = 17^s$

   _____

3. $y = 10^x$

   _____

4. $A = 3^B$

   _____

5. $y = 2^t$

   _____

In problems 6-10, write the logarithmic equation in exponential form.

6. $\log_3 x = y$

   _____

7. $\log_N A = Z$

   _____

8. $\log_B W = Q$

   _____

9. $\ln x = y$

   _____

10. $\log_{22} x = y$

    _____

In problems 11-22, solve the given equation for x. Round your answers to the nearest millionth.

11. $10^x = 20$

12. $10^x = 117$

_____

_____

13. $1,000 = 10^{2x-1}$

14. $1,234 = 10^{3x+2}$

_____

_____

15. $\log_5 x = 2$

16. $\log_3 x = 4$

_____

_____

17. $\log_2 x = 8$

18. $\log_4 x = 2$

_____

_____

19. $\ln(8 - 3x) = 7$

20. $\ln(3 + 3x) = 3$

_____

_____

21. $\ln(7x - 4) = 2$

22. $\ln(5 + 6x) = -3$

_____

_____

In problems 23-27, solve the given equation for x.

23. $\log_5(7x + 1) = -1$

24. $\log_2(5x + 3) = -2$

_____

_____

25. $\log_3(4x + 9) = -2$

26. $\log_7(3 - 4x) = 2$

_____

_____

27. $\log_9(2 - 6x) = 1$

_____

In problems 28-32, graph the given function.

28. $f(x) = \log(3 - x)$

29. $g(x) = \log(2x + 3)$

_____ _____

30. $h(x) = \ln(5x - 10)$

31. $f(x) = \ln(4 - 2x)$

_____ _____

32. $H(x) = -\ln(5 - 3x)$

_____

Problems

1. $\log_9 1 = ?$

_____

2. $\log_2 1 = ?$

_____

3. $\log_{13} 13 = ?$

_____

4. $\log_8 8 = ?$

_____

5. $\ln e = ?$

_____

6. $\log_3 9 = ?$

_____

7. $\log_2 32 = ?$

_____

8. $\log_4 64 = ?$

_____

9. $\log_5 625 = ?$

_____

10. $\log_6 36 = ?$

_____

11. $\log_5 125 = ?$

_____

12. $\log_3 81 = ?$

_____

13. $\log_2 128 = ?$

_____

14. $\log_2 2^{100} = ?$

_____

15. $\log 1,000 = ?$

_____

16. $\log 1,000,000,000,000 = ?$

_____

17. $\log 0.000001 = ?$

_____

18. $\log 0.0001 = ?$

_____

For problems 19-27, assume that $\log_b a = 4$ *and* $\log_b c = -5$.

19. $\log_b\left(a^3 c^2\right) = ?$

20. $\log_b\left(a^5 c^4\right) = ?$

_____

_____

21. $\log_b\left(\dfrac{a^8}{c^7}\right) = ?$

22. $\log_b\left(\dfrac{\sqrt[4]{a^3}}{\sqrt[5]{c^2}}\right) = ?$

_____

_____

23. $\log_b\left(\dfrac{\sqrt[7]{a^4}}{\sqrt[5]{c^3}}\right) = ?$

24. $\log_b\left(\dfrac{\sqrt[3]{a}}{\sqrt{c}}\right) = ?$

_____

_____

25. $\log_b\left(\dfrac{\sqrt[3]{a^2 c}}{\sqrt[5]{ac^2}}\right) = ?$

26. $\log_b\left(\dfrac{\sqrt[3]{a}\sqrt{c}}{\sqrt{a}\sqrt[3]{c}}\right)$

_____

_____

27. $\log_b\left(\dfrac{\sqrt[6]{a^5}\sqrt{c}}{\sqrt[5]{c^2}\sqrt{a}}\right) = ?$

_____

For problems 28-33, write the expression as a single logarithm; use radical notation.

28. $\dfrac{5\log_b V}{7} - \dfrac{3\log_b W}{7}$

29. $\dfrac{2\log_\psi x}{3} + 3\log_\psi y$

_____

_____

30. $7\log_2 u - \dfrac{\log_2 v}{5}$

31. $\dfrac{3\log_B x}{4} + \dfrac{\log_B y}{2}$

_____

_____

32. $\dfrac{\log_3 x}{2} - 2\log_3 y$

33. $\dfrac{2\log_B W - \log_B Q}{5}$

_____

_____

For problems 34-40, round your answers to the nearest millionth.

34. $\log_3 25 = ?$

35. $\log_5 33 = ?$

36. $\log 255 = ?$

37. $\log 7777 = ?$

38. $\ln 25 = ?$

39. $\ln 100 = ?$

40. $\log_{13} 100 - \log_{13} 0.1 = ?$

Problems

Solve the equation in problems 1-17.
Round your solutions to the nearest millionth (unless your answer is exact).

1. $2^x = 10$

_____

2. $5^x = 10$

_____

3. $7^{3-2x} = 9$

_____

4. $2^{8x-9} = 3$

_____

5.   Solve: $2^{3x-5} = 8$

_____

6.   Solve: $5^{4x+1} = 625$

_____

7. $5^{4x+7} = 7^{6-8x}$

_____

8. $2^{9x+1} = 3^{5-4x}$

_____

9. $6^{5x-3} = 4^{2x+1}$

_____

10. $7^{7x-7} = 6^{6x+6}$

_____

11. $e^{-0.03t} = 8$

_____

12. $e^{0.49x} = 100$

_____

13. $e^{-0.71y} = 0.5$

_____

14. $e^{4.1z} = 4.1$

_____

15. $2^{2^x} = 22$

_____

16. $3^{4^y} = 34$

_____

17. $10^{2^z} = 1000$

_____

In problems 18-35, find all solutions to the given equation.
Round your solutions to the nearest millionth (unless your answer is exact).

18. $2^{x^2} \cdot 2^{4x} = 32$

19. $3^{6x^2} \cdot 3^{-7x} = \dfrac{1}{9}$

_____

20. $5^{25x^2} \cdot 5^{5x} = 25$

21. $\log_2(5 - 2x) = 2$

_____

22. $\log_5(7x + 3) + 5 = 6$

23. $\log_3(5x - 2) - 2 = 1$

_____

24. $\log_4(7x - 3) = 3$

25. $\log_7(1 - 8x) - 2 = 0$

_____

26. $\log_5(9x + 3) = \log_5(6 - 7x)$

27. $\log_9(2x - 5) = \log_9(3 + x)$

_____

28. $\log_{17}\left(9x^2 - 7x + 13\right) = \log_{17}\left(8x^2 + 1\right)$

29. $\log_2\left(5x^2 - 10x\right) = \log_2\left(3x^2 - 4x + 80\right)$

_____

30. $\log_3(x - 3) + \log_3(x + 3) = 3$

31. $\log_9(x - 4) + \log_9(x + 4) = 2$

_____

32. $\log_{16}(2x + 1) + \log_{16}(2x - 1) = 1$

33. $\log_3(5x - 2) + \log_3(5x + 2) = 3$

_____

34. $\ln(1 - 6x) + \ln(1 - 4x) = 2$

35. $\ln(3x - 1) + \ln(x - 3) = 3$

_____

Solve the equation in problems 36-41.
Round your solutions to the nearest millionth (unless your answer is exact).

36. $\ln(3-2x) - \ln(4x+1) = 1$

37. $\log(3x-1) - \log(3x+1) = 1$

_____

_____

38. $\log_4(x+3) - \log_4 x = 2$

39. $\log_2(7x+5) - \log_2 x = 3$

_____

_____

40. $\log_3(13x+1) - \log_3(2x) = 2$

41. $\log_3(14x+3) - \log_3(4x) = 2$

_____

_____

Chapter 8 Section 6: Applications of Exponentials and Logarithms

Problems

In problems 1-14, assume an unconstrained population growth model.

1. The population of Erehwon (in millions) can be modeled by the equation
    $$P(t) = 22e^{0.022t}.$$

    What is the doubling time of the Erehwon's population, to the nearest month?

    _____

2. The population of Mordor can be modeled by the equation
    $$P(t) = 50005e^{0.005t}.$$

    What is the doubling time of the Mordor's population, to the nearest month?

    _____

3. The population of Nagadan (in millions) can be modeled by the equation
    $$P(t) = 76e^{0.035t}.$$

    What is the doubling time of the Nagadan's population, to the nearest month?

    _____

4. The population of Neverland (in thousands) can be modeled by the equation
    $$P(t) = 9e^{0.015t}.$$

    What is the doubling time of the Neverland's population, to the nearest month?

    _____

5. The population of planet Papagad (in billions) can be modeled by the equation
    $$P(t) = 1.8\,e^{0.05t}.$$

    What is the doubling time of the Papagad's population, to the nearest month?

    _____

6. The population of Planet ABC was 3.3 billion, one hundred years ago. Currently the population is 3.5 billion. What will this population be 100 years from now? Round to the nearest tenth of a billion.)

    _____

7. E. coli bacteria have a doubling time of 20 minutes. Starting with 120 E. coli bacteria, how many will there be 5 hours later?

    _____

8. A bacteria population has a doubling time of 12 minutes. How large will an initial population of 100 bacteria grow to after 3 hours?

   _____

9 A bacteria population has a doubling time of 5 minutes. How large will an initial population of 300 bacteria grow to after 2 hours?

   _____

10. A bacteria population has a doubling time of 34 minutes. How large will an initial population of 1 bacterium become after 1 hour?

    _____

11. A bacteria population is initially 1,000. After 30 minutes, they've grown in number to 3,450. How long does it take to grow to a population of 1,000,000? (round your answer to the nearest minute.)

    _____

12. A bacteria population is initially 369. After 27 minutes, they've grown in number to 590. How long does it take to grow to a population of 2,000,000? (round your answer to the nearest minute.)

    _____

13. A bacteria population is initially 123. After 45 minutes, they've grown in number to 1,234. What is the doubling time for this population? (Round your answer to the nearest second.)

    _____

14. A bacteria population is initially 137. After 40 minutes, they've grown in number to 731. What is the doubling time for this population? (Round your answer to the nearest second.)

    _____

15. The radioactive substance *18F-fluoro-deoxyglucose*, with a half-life of 110 minutes, is used in Positron Emission Tomography (PET). If you start off with 100 grams of *18F-fluoro-deoxyglucose*, how much will remain after 8 hours? (Round your answer to the nearest hundredth of a gram.)

    _____

16. The radioactive substance polonium-210, with a half-life of 138.39 days is present in tobacco. Suppose that an ex- smoker's lungs contain 800 milligrams of polonium-210. How much radioactive polonium will remain after one year of not smoking? (Round your answer to the nearest milligram.)

    _____

17.   An initial sample of 100 grams of plutonium-239 decays to 99.715861 grams after 100 years. What is the half-life? (Round your answer to the nearest hundred.)

_____

18.   An initial sample of 1 gram of plutonium-239 decays to 0.99715861 grams after 100 years. How long will it take one gram of plutonium to decay to one microgram (one millionth of a gram)? (Round your answer to the nearest year.)

_____

19.   Plutonium-239 has a half-life of about 24,400 years. How long before 20,000 kilograms of plutonium decays down to 1 microgram?

_____

20.   What is the half-life of Radium-226, if a sample of 100 grams decays to 99.956674 grams after one year? (Round your answer to the nearest year.)

_____

21.   What is the half-life of Cesium-137, if a sample of 20 grams decays to 19.09683208 grams after two years? (round your answer to the nearest year.)

_____

22.   Carbon-14 has a half-life of 5,750 years. Suppose that a sample is found to have 17% its original carbon-14. How old is the sample? (Round to the nearest year.)

_____

23.   An ancient boat was found preserved in clay sediments in Naples, Italy. A wood sample form the boat was found to have 73% its original carbon-14. How old is the sample (carbon-14 has a half-life of 5,750 years)? (Round to the nearest year.)

_____

24.   A piece of cloth was found to have 92.14% of its original carbon-14 (carbon-14 has a half-life of 5,750 years). How old is this artifact? (Round to the nearest year.)

_____

25.   A manuscript is alleged to be 1500 years old. If it currently has 97% of its original carbon-14 (carbon-14 has a half-life of 5,750 years). How old is the manuscript? Is it a forgery? (round the nearest year.)

_____

26.   Carbon-14 has a half-life of 5,750 years. Human bones are found at a construction site—a possible murder victim. If the bones are found to contain 99.5% of their original carbon-14, how long ago was the murder committed? (round to the nearest year.)

_____

27. Carbon-14 has a half-life of 5,750 years. For an artifact to be considered 3,000 years old, what percentage of it original carbon-14 must remain in the artifact? (Round to the nearest tenth of a percent.)

   _____

28. Carbon-14 has a half-life of 5.750 years. For an artifact to be considered 10,000 years old, what percentage of its original carbon-14 would remain in the artifact? (Round to the nearest hundredth of a percent.)

   _____

In problem 29 – 36, assume all interest is compounded continuously.

29. How much money should you invest in a stock earning 20% annual interest, in order for it to grow to one million dollars in 20 years?

   _____

30. How much money should you invest in a stock earning 5% annual interest, in order for it to grow to one million dollars in 20 years?

   _____

31. How much money should you invest in a stock earning 6% annual interest, in order for it to grow to one million dollars in 40 years?

   _____

32. What annual interest rate r would be needed in order for $10,000 to grow to $1,000,000 in 30 years (round your answer to the nearest hundredth of a percent.)

   _____

33. Suppose you could go back in time 400 years. How much should you deposit into an account earning 4% annual interest for it to be work $100,000,000 now?

   _____

34. If you purchased one share of the initial offering of Company A's stock back in 1986 for $21 it would be worth about $10,000 in 2004. What was the annual interest rate of this investment? (round your answer to the nearest hundredth of a percent.)

   _____

35. Suppose in a vivid dream you meet your future self, who convinces you to invest in a company called Sentient Machines Incorporated. Your future self assures you that an investment of $1,000 now will net you $25,000,000 in 30 years. If true, what will have been the annual interest rate of return of your investment? (Round your answer to the nearest hundredth of a percent.)

   _____

36. Suppose in a vivid dream you meet your future self, who give you a stock tip. Your future self assures you that an investment of $100,000 now will net you $100,000,000 in 25 years. If true, what will have been the annual interest rate of return of your investment? (Round your answer to the nearest hundredth of a percent.)

_____

37. The number of bits of information transmitted when message m is received, is given by

$$I(m) = \log_2\left(\frac{1}{Prob(m)}\right)$$

where $Prob(m)$ is the probability that message m would b received. Suppose that the probability of a particular message being received is 0.01. How many bits of information are transmitted when this message is received? (Round your answer to the nearest hundredth of a bit.)

_____

38. The number of bits of information transmitted when message m is received, is given by

$$I(m) = \log_2\left(\frac{1}{Prob(m)}\right)$$

where $Prob(m)$ is the probability that message m would b received. Suppose that the probability of a particular message being received is 0.5. How many bits of information are transmitted when this message is received? (Round your answer to the nearest hundredth of a bit.)

_____

39. The number of bits of information transmitted when message m is received, is given by

$$I(m) = \log_2\left(\frac{1}{Prob(m)}\right)$$

where $Prob(m)$ is the probability that message m would b received. If a message transmits 10 bits of information, what was the probability of receiving this message? (Round your answer to the nearest thousandth.)

_____

40. The number of bits of information transmitted when message m is received, is given by

$$I(m) = \log_2\left(\frac{1}{Prob(m)}\right)$$

where $Prob(m)$ is the probability that message m would b received. If a message transmits 10 bits of information, what was the probability of receiving this message? (Round your answer to the nearest thousandth.)

_____

Intermediate Algebra 2ND Edition
Practice Problem Worksheets

Chapter 9: The Conic Sections

Problems

For problems 1-20, find the vertex of the given parabola.

1. $y = x^2 - 6x + 2$

2. $y = x^2 - 8x - 9$

3. $y = 2x^2 + 4x + 7$

4. $y = -3x^2 + 5x - 1$

5. $y = -6x^2 + 12x + 5$

6. $y = -10x^2 + 40x - 57$

7. $y = -2x^2 + 28x - 97$

8. $y = -12x^2 + 48x - 43$

9. $y = -x^2 + 6x - 2$

10. $y = 21x^2 - 84x + 91$

11. $x = 4y^2 - 16y + 3$

12. $x = -5y^2 + 20y - 13$

13. $x = 7y^2 - 28y + 25$

14. $x = -5y^2 - 70y - 238$

15. $x = 9y^2 + 36y + 38$

16. $x = -8y^2 + 64y - 123$

17. $x = y^2 - y - 1$

18. $x = -y^2 + 2y - 3$

19. $x = 4y^2 + 17$

20. $x = -9y^2 + 36y - 35$

For problems 21-30, find the x- and y-intercepts of the given parabola.

21. $y = x^2 - 6x + 2$

22. $y = x^2 - 8x - 9$

_____

_____

23. $y = 2x^2 + 4x + 7$

24. $y = -3x^2 + 5x - 1$

_____

_____

25. $y = -6x^2 + 12x + 5$

26. $x = 4y^2 - 16y + 3$

_____

_____

27. $x = -5y^2 + 20y - 13$

28. $x = y^2 - y - 1$

_____

_____

29. $x = -y^2 + 2y - 3$

30. $x = 4y^2 + 17$

_____

_____

Graph each equation in problems 31-40.

31. $y = x^2 - 6x + 2$

32. $y = x^2 - 8x - 9$

33. $y = 2x^2 + 4x + 7$

34. $y = -3x^2 + 5x - 1$

---

35. $y = -6x^2 + 12x + 5$

36. $x = 4y^2 - 16y + 3$

---

37. $x = -5y^2 + 20y - 13$

38. $x = y^2 - y - 1$

---

39. $x = -y^2 + 2y - 3$

40. $x = 4y^2 + 17$

Problems

Find the distance between the given points, for problems 1 through 6. Also give decimal approximations to your exact solutions.

1. (2,5) and (4,8)

2. (–1,2) and (5, –4)

_____

_____

3. (5, –1) and (–6,7)

4. (–2,8) and (–4,5)

_____

_____

5. (–9, –7) and (3, –9)

6. (4, –2) and (4, –5)

_____

_____

For problems 7 through 12, find the equation of the circle with the given radius and center.

7. radius = 6, center = (–3,9)

8. radius = 1, center = (–2,–3)

_____

_____

9. radius = 5, center = (10,–13)

10. radius = 13, center = (5,7)

_____

_____

11. radius = 11, center = (–33, –22)

12. radius = 7, center = (5,–8)

_____

_____

Find the equation of the given circle, for problems 13 through 18.

13.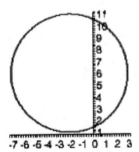

14.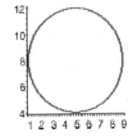

_____

_____

15.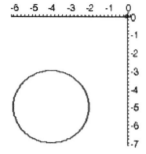

16.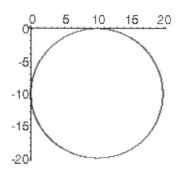

_____

17.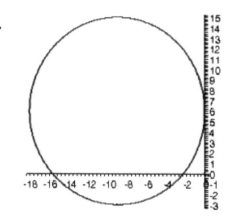

18.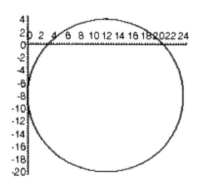

_____

Find the radius and center of the circle defined by the given equation, for problems 19 through 36.

19. $(x-8)^2 + (y-2)^2 = 36$

20. $(x+18)^2 + (y-12)^2 = 100$

_____

21. $(x-63)^2 + (y+77)^2 = 169$

22. $(x+23)^2 + (y+32)^2 = 400$

_____

23. $(x-3)^2 + (y-2)^2 = 1$

24. $(x+17)^2 + (y-71)^2 = 81$

_____

25. $x^2 + y^2 - 6x + 10y - 15 = 0$

26. $x^2 + y^2 + 16x - 12y + 84 = 0$

_____

27. $x^2 + y^2 + 6x + 8y + 24 = 0$

28. $x^2 + y^2 - 16y - 36 = 0$

_____

_____

29. $x^2 + y^2 - 10x + 10y + 25 = 0$

30. $x^2 + y^2 + 14x - 6y + 22 = 0$

_____

_____

31. $x^2 + y^2 + 2x - 4y + 3 = 0$

32. $x^2 + y^2 - 6x - 2y - 1 = 0$

_____

_____

33. $x^2 + y^2 + 8x - 6y + 5 = 0$

34. $x^2 + y^2 - 12x + 14y + 2 = 0$

_____

_____

35. $x^2 + y^2 - 24x - 8y + 70 = 0$

36. $x^2 + y^2 + 14x + 18y - 17 = 0$

_____

_____

Graph the circles in problems 37 through 44.

37. $x^2 + y^2 = 25$

38. $x^2 + y^2 = 9$

_____

_____

39. $x^2 + y^2 = 49$

40. $x^2 + y^2 = 144$

_____

_____

41. $x^2 + y^2 + 2x + 4y - 13 = 0$

42. $x^2 + y^2 - 6x + 8y - 10 = 0$

---

43. $x^2 + y^2 + 22x - 14y + 12 = 0$

44. $x^2 + y^2 + 10x + 16y - 17 = 0$

---

45. Find two functions f_T and f_B, whose graphs together form the circle:
$$(x - 1)^2 + (y - 2)^2 = 3$$

46. Find two functions f_T and f_B, whose graphs together form the circle:
$$(x - 5)^2 + (y - 6)^2 = 7$$

---

47. Find two functions f_T and f_B, whose graphs together form the circle:
$$(x + 4)^2 + (y + 1)^2 = 9$$

48. Find two functions f_T and f_B, whose graphs together form the circle:
$$(x + 5)^2 + (y + 8)^2 = 3$$

---

49. Find two functions f_T and f_B, whose graphs together form the circle:
$$(x + 2)^2 + (y - 3)^2 = 4$$

50. Find two functions f_T and f_B, whose graphs together form the circle:
$$(x - 7)^2 + (y + 9)^2 = 2$$

Problems

Graph the ellipses in problems 1 through 6.

1. $\dfrac{x^2}{4} + \dfrac{y^2}{25} = 1$

2. $\dfrac{x^2}{9} + \dfrac{y^2}{4} = 1$

3. $\dfrac{x^2}{16} + \dfrac{y^2}{9} = 1$

4. $\dfrac{x^2}{36} + \dfrac{y^2}{25} = 1$

5. $\dfrac{x^2}{81} + \dfrac{y^2}{4} = 1$

6. $\dfrac{x^2}{4} + y^2 = 1$

Chapter 9 Section 3: Ellipses

Find the equation of the ellipse shown, for problems 7 through 12.

7.

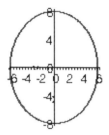

_____

8.

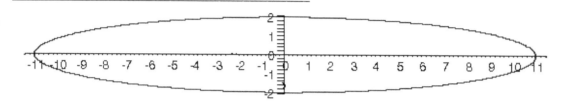

_____

9.   **10.**

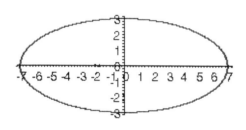   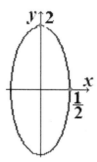

_____   _____

11.

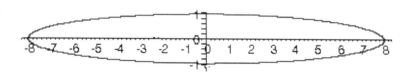

_____

12.

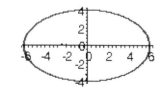

_____

Graph the ellipses in problems 13 through 18.

13. $\dfrac{(x-1)^2}{9} + \dfrac{(y-4)^2}{4} = 1$

14. $\dfrac{(x-4)^2}{9} + \dfrac{(y+2)^2}{4} = 1$

_____   _____

15. $\dfrac{(x+2)^2}{16} + \dfrac{(y-1)^2}{9} = 1$

16. $\dfrac{(x+6)^2}{36} + \dfrac{(y+5)^2}{25} = 1$

_____   _____

17. $\dfrac{(x-3)^2}{81} + \dfrac{(y+3)^2}{4} = 1$

18. $\dfrac{x^2}{4} + (y-2)^2 = 1$

_____   _____

Find the equation of the ellipse shown, for problems 19 through 24.

19.

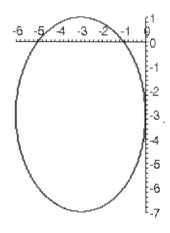

20.

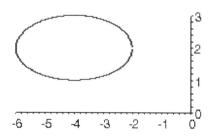

_____

21.

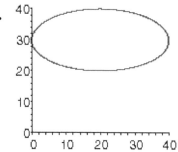

22.

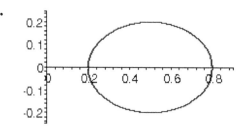

_____

23.

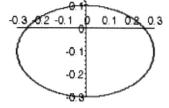

24.

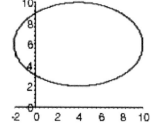

_____

Graph the ellipses in problems 25 through 30.

25. $4(y-7)^2 = 25\left(196-(x+7)^2\right)$

26. $4(x+3)^2 = 29\left(4-(y-2)^2\right)$

_____

_____

27. $49\left((y-2)^2-1\right) = -(x+3)^2$

28. $2\left(y+\sqrt{5}\right)^2 = 10-5\left(x+\sqrt{5}\right)^2$

_____

_____

29. $(y-1)^2 = 7\left(1-\dfrac{(x-2)^2}{3}\right)$

30. $3y^2 = 12-4(x+1)^2$

_____

_____

Problems

Graph each hyperbola.

1. $\dfrac{x^2}{25} - \dfrac{y^2}{16} = 1$

2. $\dfrac{x^2}{25} - \dfrac{y^2}{9} = 1$

3. $x^2 - 16y^2 = 1$

4. $9x^2 - \dfrac{y^2}{4} = 1$

5. $\dfrac{x^2}{9} - \dfrac{y^2}{10} = 1$

6. $\dfrac{y^2}{4} - \dfrac{x^2}{16} = 1$

7. $\dfrac{y^2}{9} - \dfrac{x^2}{25} = 1$

8. $\dfrac{y^2}{25} - \dfrac{x^2}{36} = 1$

_____

_____

9. $y^2 - 4x^2 = 1$

10. $\dfrac{y^2}{3} - \dfrac{x^2}{10} = 1$

_____

_____

11. $\dfrac{(2x + 3y)(2x - 3y)}{9} = 4$

12. $(2x + y)(2x - y) = 4$

_____

_____

13. $(3x - 2y)(3x + 2y) = 36$

14. $(5x - 2y)(5x + 2y) = 200$

_____

_____

15. $\left(\dfrac{x}{6} - \dfrac{y}{2}\right)\left(\dfrac{x}{6} + \dfrac{y}{2}\right) = 1$

16. $(2y + x)(2y - x) = 4$

_____

_____

17. $xy = 9$

18. $xy = 25$

_____

_____

19. $xy = 100$

20. $xy = 10$

_____

_____

21. $x = \dfrac{4}{y}$

22. $x = \dfrac{2}{y}$

_____

_____

23. $xy = -36$

24. $xy = -100$

_____

_____

25. $3x = \dfrac{27}{y}$

26. $2x = -\dfrac{16}{y}$

_____

_____

27. $\left(2x - 3y\right)^2 = 1 + \left(2x + 3y\right)^2$

28. $\left(5x - 6y\right)^2 = 120 + \left(5x + 6y\right)^2$

_____

_____

Problems

Solve the following nonlinear systems.

Nonlinear System	**Graph**	**Intersection Points**
1. $y = x + 1$ $x^2 + y^2 = 9$	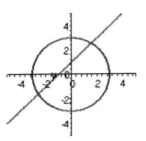	_____
2. $y = 2x + 1$ $xy = 4$	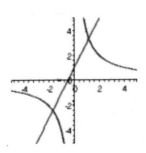	_____
3. $x + 3y = 1$ $x^2 - y^2 = 2$	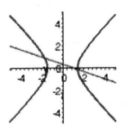	_____
4. $y = 2x - 3$ $x^2 + y = 9$	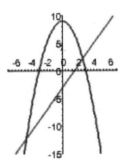	_____
5. $y = x + 1$ $\dfrac{x^2}{25} + \dfrac{y^2}{16} = 1$	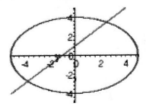	_____

Nonlinear System	**Graph**	**Intersection Points**

6. $xy = 3$

$y = x^2$

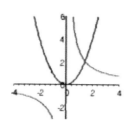

_____

7. $x^2 y = 1$

$x^2 = 2 - y$

_____

8. $x + y = 1$

$xy = -1$

_____

9. $yx = 2$

$y - x = 2$

_____

10. $xy = 1$

$x - y^2 = 0$

_____

11. $y = \sqrt{15} \cdot x^2$

$x^2 + y^2 = 16$

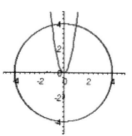

_____

Nonlinear System	**Graph**	**Intersection Points**
12. $y = 2x^2$ $x = 2y^2$	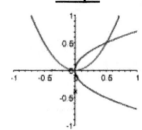	_____
13. $y = -x^2 - x + 7$ $y = 2x + 1$	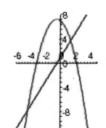	_____
14. $y = 1 - x^2$ $x^2 + y^2 = 1$	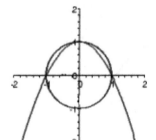	_____
15. $\dfrac{x^2}{4} + y^2 = 1$ $x^2 + \dfrac{y^2}{4} = 2$	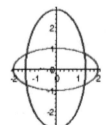	_____
16. $\dfrac{x}{3} + \dfrac{y}{4} = 1$ $\dfrac{x^2}{9} + \dfrac{y^2}{4} = 1$	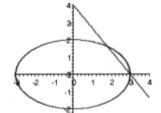	_____
17. $y = 1 - 3x^2$ $y = x^2 - 3$	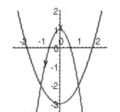	_____

Nonlinear System	**Graph**	**Intersection Points**

18. $(x+1)^2 + y^2 = 4$

$(x-1)^2 + y^2 = 4$

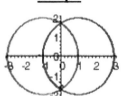

_____

19. $y = 1 - 4x^2$

$x = 1 - 4y^2$

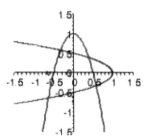

_____

20. $x^2 + (y-5)^2 = 4$

$x^2 + y^2 = 16$

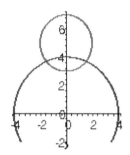

_____

21. $xy^2 = 4 - y^2$

$xy^2 = 2y^2 - 1$

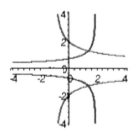

_____

22. $x^2 y = 4 - y$

$x^2 y = 2y - 1$

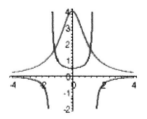

_____

23. $x^2 y^3 = 1$

$x^2 y^3 = 2y - 1$

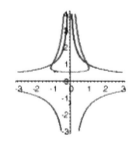

_____

CPSIA information can be obtained
at www.ICGtesting.com
Printed in the USA
LVHW062019200320
650729LV00004B/15